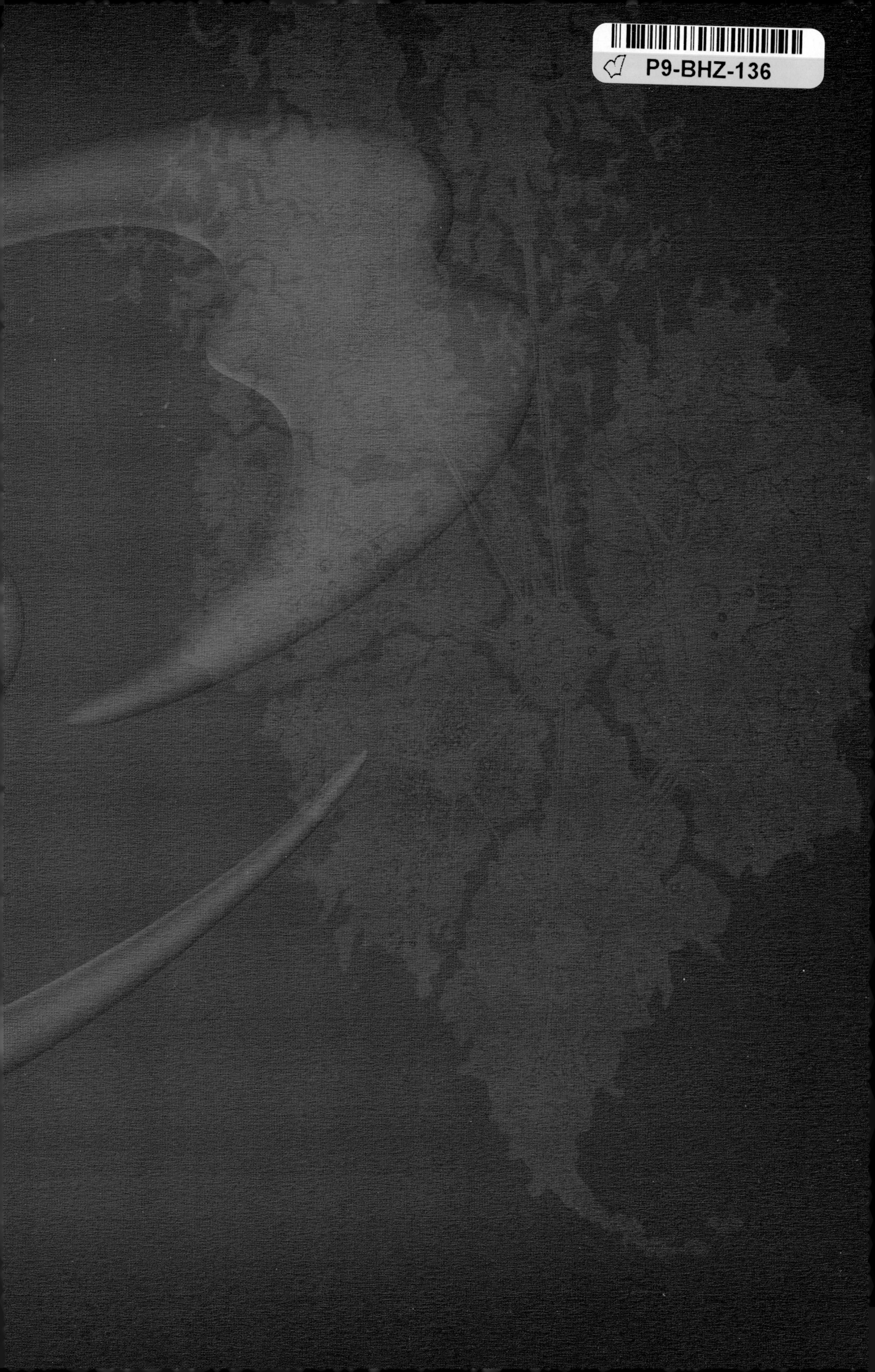

AMEET Sp. z o.o.
Przybyszewskiego 176/178, 93-120 Łódź – Poland
ameet@ameet.com.pl, www.ameet.pl

Printed in Poland

MAKUTA'S DIARY

I AM MAKUTA TERIDAX, AND THIS IS THE STORY OF HOW I CAME TO BE THE SUPREME RULER OF ALL THAT IS AND ALL THAT EVER WILL BE IN THIS UNIVERSE. IN THE BEGINNING, THE GREAT BEINGS CREATED A UNIVERSE, FILLED IT WITH LIFE, AND APPOINTED THE GREAT SPIRIT MATA NUI TO WATCH OVER IT. MATA NUI CREATED MYSELF AND MY FELLOW MAKUTA TO HELP HIM.

FOR THOUSANDS OF YEARS, WE CREATED THE BEASTS THAT ROAMED AND SWAM AND FLEW. WE WATCHED OVER THE MATORAN VILLAGERS AND PROTECTED THE PEACE. AND THEN CAME A DAY WHEN WE LED OUR ARMIES AGAINST THE REBELLIOUS BARRAKI WARLORDS, DEFEATING THEM. THEY HAD HOPED TO OVERTHROW MATA NUI AND SEIZE POWER. THAT WAS WHEN I REALIZED THAT THEY COULD NEVER HOPE TO ACHIEVE SUCH A GOAL... BUT I COULD DO IT. I COULD RULE A UNIVERSE!

METRU NUI

Known as the "city of legends," Metru Nui is the northernmost island in the BIONICLE® universe. It was one of the first places built by the Great Beings and has been home to Matoran villagers for almost 100,000 years. In the past, Metru Nui was a busy seaport, visited by trading ships from other islands and continents.

Metru Nui is divided into six districts, or "metru," each home to a different tribe of Matoran. It is ruled by a village elder called a Turaga. Vital work is done in Metru Nui, including the creation of Masks of Power. The jobs done by the Matoran here are so important that the Great Spirit's health seems to depend on them – if the Matoran of Metru Nui stop working for a long time, Mata Nui becomes ill.

Landmarks of Metru Nui include the Coliseum; the Great Temple; the Archives; and the Great Furnace. The city is also home to many different kinds of Rahi beasts, which migrate from the south only to be captured and put on display in the Archives.

Metru Nui has been the site of many famous events, including:

- The battle between Toa Lhikan's team and the Kanohi Dragon.
- The Toa-Dark Hunter conflict.
- The Matoran Civil War.
- The creation of the Toa Metru.

The Matoran Civil War (also known as the "Great Disruption") took place over 79,000 years ago, and began with a dispute between Ta-Metru and Po-Metru. It soon spread to include the entire city. Battles raged over four centuries, during which time virtually no work was done in the city. It was finally brought to an end through the intervention of Makuta Teridax. In the wake of the war, it was decided by the Brotherhood that a Makuta would watch over all inhabited regions of the universe to insure such a thing would not happen again. (Mata Nui was so severely weakened by the 400 year long lack of Matoran labor in Metru Nui that a team led by Toa Jovan had to take action. They sought out the Mask of Life and used it to revive the Great Spirit's failing energies.)

The city's importance is expected to continue to grow in the future.

PO-METRU

A wild, barren place, dotted with mountains and canyons, Po-Metru is home to talented Matoran stone carvers. The Matoran of Po-Metru live in caves and assemblers' villages. They are known for the huge statues they carve from slabs of rock and their skill at assembling goods.

ONU-METRU

The inhabitants of Onu-Metru live and work underground. This district is the site of the protodermis mines and the famous Archives. Solid blocks of protodermis are shipped from here to Po-Metru for carving, and any wild Rahi caught in the city were sent here to be placed in the Archives.

THE ARCHIVES

A massive underground museum, the Archives is as large as the entire city of Metru Nui. Exhibits include virtually every tool, artifact and creature ever seen on Metru Nui. The Archives features so many levels, sub-levels, and winding passageways that it is easy for a visitor to get lost. The chance of escaped Rahi roaming the halls makes the Archives a dangerous place to work.

KO-METRU

A place of great crystal buildings, Ko-Metru is dedicated to learning and research. Every written record of Metru Nui's past is kept here, along with prophecies of the future. The Knowledge Towers of the metru were not built, but grown, using special knowledge crystals. Once placed in a "cradle" somewhere in the district, the crystal would rapidly grow into a giant tower large enough to hold many Matoran.

LE-METRU

The transportation center of Metru Nui, Le-Metru is where vehicles are made and the complex chute system used for mass transit is maintained. Tangled masses of cables are everywhere and the Le-Matoran climb, swing and scramble among them as they do their work.

GA-METRU

Spiritual and educational center of the city, Ga-Metru is home to the Great Temple and many schools. It is a peaceful and beautiful place, known for its canals and fountains. Much of the daily work done in the metru is done by members of other tribes so that Ga-Matoran can be free to study.

GREAT TEMPLE

One of the most important buildings in Metru Nui, the Great Temple is dedicated to Mata Nui. The temple is the site of the Toa suva, a round stone structure believed by many to be the source of Toa power. The Great Temple has been badly damaged a number of times over the years, but always rebuilt bigger and more beautiful than before.

TA-METRU

Filled with factories and foundries, Ta-Metru is home to the skilled workers who make tools, equipment, Masks of Power, and all the other items used in the city. Molten protodermis is piped into the metru, then poured into molds and cooled. The air in Ta-Metru is always filled with smoke and steam and the temperature there is too hot for most other Matoran.

THE COLISEUM

The tallest building in Metru Nui, the Coliseum is the site of the city's government chambers, a sports arena, and a large power station. Lower levels of the Coliseum were used for storage and as cells for captured Dark Hunters and other lawbreakers. The Coliseum sits at the point where all six metru meet and it's said it belongs to everyone in the city.

TOA LHIKAN

Toa Lhikan giving a Toa stone to Vakama

This Toa of Fire led a team that defended the city of Metru Nui in ages past. They performed many heroic deeds, and Lhikan himself became a legend among the Matora of that city. A statue of him stands there to this day, honoring his courage.

Little is known about Toa Lhikan's past, as he rarely liked to speak of it. It has been confirmed th he was active as a Matoran 17,500 years ago, when he was rescued by a Toa of Fire named Dum He became a Toa 7005 years ago and was assigned to guard a strategic outpost with a team of oth heroes. Inside the outpost was an artifact of great value, the Makoki stone. Although it looked li just another stone tablet, it was inscribed with secret information about the Brotherhood of Makut

The small island was overrun by savage creatures called frostelus. Lhikan was ordered to get th Makoki stone and escape, but it had already been stolen by two thieves, Vezok and Hakann. (The Da Hunters later took the stone from them and used it to ransom their agents after the end of the To Dark Hunter war.) Lhikan followed his orders and escaped the island, the sole survivor of that tear

When the Kanohi Dragon menaced Metru Nui, Lhikan joined with 10 other Toa and fought month-long battle to defeat it. After the fight, the team remained to guard the city. Over time, son of the members left to adventure elsewhere, leaving Lhikan, Toa Nidhiki and Toa Tuyet behind. It we at this time that Tuyet attempted to seize power by stealing the energies of other Toa. She we defeated by Lhikan and Nidhiki and exiled to the Pit.

Lhikan

Turaga Lhikan

Some years later, the Dark Hunters launched an invasion of Metru Nui. Lhikan led a victorious army of Toa against them, but the victory was not without a price. Toa Nidhiki had betrayed his friends to the enemy and Lhikan had to banish him from the city. Nidhiki joined the Dark Hunters.

After Makuta Teridax took over Metru Nui by disguising himself as the city's leader, he hired the Dark Hunters to get rid of Lhikan and his teammates. Sensing danger, Lhikan acted to create a new team of Toa – the Toa Metru – to protect the city. Captured by two Dark Hunters, including his ex-teammate Nidhiki, Lhikan managed to escape. Having achieved his destiny by bringing the Toa Metru into being, Lhikan transformed from a Toa to a Turaga.

Lhikan's wisdom and experience helped the new Toa master their powers. During the final battle with Makuta Teridax, Lhikan leapt in front of a blast meant for Toa Vakama and was killed. The Toa Metru retrieved his mask and later gave it to Jaller, a Ta-Matoran.

- Although the Matoran lost their memories of Lhikan and Metru Nui later, the Toa Metru still wanted to keep his legend alive. So they created tales of "Lhii," a champion lava surfer, and his heroic acts.

- Lhikan has appeared in a pair of alternate timelines. In one, he and his original team were saved from the frostelus by a squad led by Toa Lesovikk. In another, Lhikan was killed by Nidhiki during the fight with Tuyet. This resulted in Tuyet taking over the universe and establishing a tyrannical Toa Empire.

- A team of Toa, the Inika, met someone who appeared to be Lhikan on the island of Voya Nui more than 1000 years after his death. This turned out to be just an illusion of the hero created to test the courage of

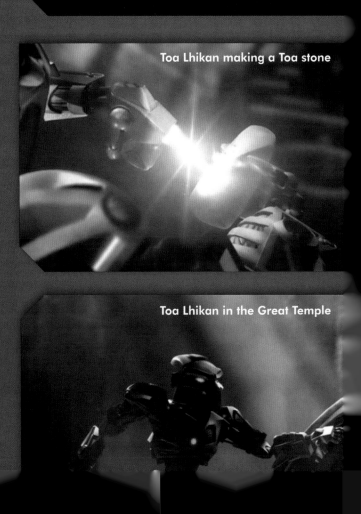

Toa Lhikan making a Toa stone

Toa Lhikan in the Great Temple

DARK HUNTERS

The Dark Hunters are thieves, bounty hunters and mercenaries under the command of a being known only as The Shadowed One. Based on the island of Odina, Dark Hunters will take on any job – lawful or unlawful – as long as the pay is good enough. Along with the Brotherhood of Makuta, they are considered one of the most dangerous organizations in the universe.

Amphibax

The Dark Hunter group was founded by The Shadowed One and another member of his species known only as "Ancient." It rapidly became both respected and feared from Metru Nui to the southern continent. Over the millennia, Dark Hunters stole treasures, eliminated Toa, kidnapped Turaga, and even overthrew the governments of entire islands. They forged a relationship with the Brotherhood of Makuta, often doing jobs for Makuta Teridax or others. The Shadowed One recruits from just about any species and the group includes a wide variety of members, even some ex-Toa. Some Dark Hunters are outcasts seeking a place to belong; others are adventurers; still others are criminals who want the chance to steal and harm and get paid for it.

Sentrakh

The organization has a firm set of rules:
- Any treasure found by a Dark Hunter on a mission must be turned over to The Shadowed One.
- Any Dark Hunter who betrays the group or tries to quit will be hunted down and eliminated.
- Anyone outside of the organization who kills a Dark Hunter will also be eliminated.

NIDHIKI

Once he was a Toa of Air, before he tried to betr the city of Metru Nui to the Dark Hunters. Exile from the city, he was mutated on orders of Th Shadowed One and became a Dark Hunter himse He was later sent back to Metru Nui to capture To Lhikan and others as part of a plan by Maku Teridax. When Nidhiki failed to stop the Toa Metr Teridax absorbed him into his own body, killing th Dark Hunter. In life, Nidhiki was capable of flig and hurling force bolts at his foes. He was a skille thief and liar.

KREKKA

Big, strong, and dumb, the most exciting thing that had ever happened to Krekka was a fight he had with Makuta Gorast (which he lost). Then he was recruited into the Dark Hunters and assigned to be Nidhiki's partner, more to keep the ex-Toa honest than anything else. He was with Nidhiki in Metru Nui during the battles with Toa Lhikan and the Toa Metru, and was killed along with him by Teridax. Krekka had the power of flight and the ability to create energy webs.

In recent times, the Dark Hunters have grown more daring. After their request to build a base on Metru Nui was refused, they invaded that city and attempted to conquer it. With the help of a traitorous Toa, Nidhiki, they almost succeeded. But their forces were tricked and ambushed by a small army of Toa. The captured Dark Hunters were shipped back to Odina and warned not to return.

Later, the Dark Hunters accepted a job helping Makuta Teridax get rid of the Toa of Metru Nui and seize control of the city. During the mission, two of the Dark Hunters were killed by Teridax. When The Shadowed One discovered this, he declared war on the Brotherhood. The war continues to rage to this day.

Recently, six members of the Dark Hunters broke away and went out on their own. Calling themselves "Piraka," they attempted to steal the powerful Mask of Life. Although the Dark Hunters sent agents to stop them, it was a team of Toa who defeated the Piraka in the end.

The Piraka

The Dark Hunters remain a very real threat to safety and peace. Their fortress on Odina was recently destroyed by Toa Nuva Pohatu, but that is a minor setback at best to an organization so powerful.

VAKAMA

Vakama was a mask maker in Metru Nui, who was asked by Turaga Dume (actually Makuta Teridax in disguise) to create a Mask of Time. Before he could do so, he was given a Toa stone by Toa Lhikan and told to bring it to the Great Temple. Vakama did so, meeting five other Matoran there. When they put their stones into the Toa suva, they were bathed in energy and transformed into the Toa Metru. Toa Vakama had a vision of six Great Kanoka Disks and the city being destroyed. He led the new team on a search for the disks and into a battle with the giant, intelligent plant called the Morbuzakh. The Toa Metru next defeated the shapeshifting creature Krahka, who threatened Metru Nui. Shortly after that, they discovered how Makuta had tricked them and that he had captured all of the city's Matoran and imprisoned them in canisters.

The Toa Metru battled Makuta, the robotic Vahki, and the Dark Hunters Nidhiki and Krekka. During this adventure, Vakama succeeded in combining the Great Disks and creating the Mask of Time. In the end, the city was shattered but the Toa were able to temporarily stop Makuta. Vakama led the Toa on a search for a new island where the Matoran could live in safety, and they named the place they discovered "Mata Nui" after the Great Spirit.

Returning to Metru Nui to begin transporting the Matoran, the Toa walked into an ambush set by Visorak spiders. Transformed by Visorak venom into a bestial Toa Hordika, Vakama betrayed his team and allied with the Visorak. He later repented and helped the other Toa defeat the Visorak and save the Matoran. Using their Toa power, Vakama and his friends were able to free the villagers. In doing so, the Toa transformed into Turaga. Vakama would become the Turaga of Fire in the village of Ta-Koro on Mata Nui.

As a Toa Metru, Vakama wore the Kanohi Huna, the Great Mask of Concealment, and carried

Later, Matau regretted his behavior. During the final battle with the Visorak, it was Matau who appealed to Vakama to return to being a hero. Matau risked his own life to remind Vakama what being a Toa was all about, and succeeded in winning Vakama back to the side of justice.

...ATAU

...tau was a Matoran of Air in ...tru Nui whose job was ...ting prototypes of new ...nicles. Being reckless and a ...er of speed, Matau ...quently crashed. During one ...y dangerous test of a ...to-sled, Matau was almost ...ed, only to be rescued by Toa ...kan. The Toa gave Matau a ...stone and told him to take ...the Great Temple.

...cing the Toa stone into the ...suva turned Matau into a ...Metru. He was thrilled. ...tau was sure that he would ...n lots of fame and glory as a ...o, but it didn't quite work ...that way. First, he was stuck ...ide a giant blast furnace, ...hting the crazed Morbuzakh ...nt.

...n he was down in the dank ...nels beneath the Archives, ...hting a Rahi beast who ...nted to take over the city. ...d after that, he was on the ...n, being hunted by the Vahki ...o had always protected his ...!

...en the Toa Metru were later ...ned into monstrous Toa ...rdika by Visorak venom, ...tau blamed Vakama. Since ...kama was their leader, ...tau felt, he should have been ...art enough not to lead the ...m into a trap. The cruel ...ngs Matau said helped to ...sh Vakama away from his ...nds and led to him joining ...enemy.

Matau went on to become the Turaga of Le-Koro on the island of Mata Nui. He became known for his sense of humor as well as his bravery, particularly enjoying playing pranks on Turaga Nuju.

As a Toa Metru, Matau wore the Kanohi Mahiki, the Great Mask of Illusion. He carried twin aero slicers which also functioned as wings.

WHENUA

Whenua was working as an archivist in Onu-Metru when Toa Lhikan gave him a Toa stone. Transfor[med] into a Toa Metru, he was not reckless like Matau or a leader like Vakama. He preferred to ana[lyze] situations before rushing into them. But no one could question his bravery as he aided in the fights ag[ainst] the Vahki and the Visorak.

Even as a Toa, Whenua felt a special connection to the Archives. It was at his urging that the Toa Metru explored them, seeking the source of a water leak that might have threatened the exhibits. What they found was Krahka and a battle to stop that Rahi from invading the city. Later, Whenua would watch with a broken heart as an earthquake ripped open the Archives, unleashing all the beasts housed there on his city.

During the Toa Metru's search for a new home for the Matoran, Whenua encountered an old friend, Mavrah. This archivist had left the city many years before and gone to live in nearby tunnels with a horde of prehistoric Rahi beasts.

Convinced the Toa were there to capture him and bring him back, he tried to destroy them. In the e[nd] Mavrah died as a result of his own actions, despite Whenua's efforts to save him.

Whenua went on to become Turaga of Onu-Koro, known for his wisdom and fairness. He had a lov[e of] history, believing the solution to many of today's problems could be found in the past.

As a Toa, Whenua wore the Kanohi Ruru, the Great Mask of Night Vision, and carried twin earthsh[aker] drills.

becoming a Toa – it took him away from his work. (Nuju once said that Toa had to be chosen by destiny for the job, because no sane being would volunteer for it.) Still, he was a powerful member of the Toa Metru, best known for his skill at solving mysteries and his ability to think ahead. He was never really comfortable being in a team, though, and often wished for the chance to simply go back to defending Ko-Metru.

When the Toa Metru turned into Toa Hordika, Nuju learned the language of the Rahi. After he became the Turaga of Ko-Koro, he would continue to only speak in that language. It was his way of reminding the others of the dangers of overconfidence and pride, the qualities that had led them into the Visorak ambush years before.

Perhaps Nuju's finest moment as a Toa came when the Toa Metru were returning to Metru Nui following their discovery of the island of Mata Nui. The team encountered a monstrous beast called the Rahi Nui, a hybrid creature with the abilities and natural tools of five other beasts. The beast badly wounded Nokama in the fight and its ability to feed on the Toa's elemental energies made it extremely dangerous. But Nuju noticed that, though the creature grew bigger when it fed, it did not grow heavier. He convinced Vakama to join with him in feeding the creature more and more elemental energy, until its size was so much greater than its mass that its atoms drifted apart and dispersed.

As a Toa Metru, Nuju wore the Kanohi Matatu, the Mask of Telekinesis, and carried twin crystal spikes.

career as a teacher in Metru Nui before becoming the Toa Metru of Water. From the start, she stood by Toa Vakama even when the others doubted him. It was she who decided Vakama should be the team leader and talked the others into it. It was also Nokama who realized the Toa Metru had to work together to defeat the Morbuzakh plant.

During the battle with Krahka, Nokama defeated three powerful Rahkshi on her own. She was the only one of the Toa Metru to avoid capture and later found and regrouped the rest of the team. As her confidence and experience grew, Nokama became one of the most effective Toa. She courageously stood alone against a rampaging herd of Kikanalo beasts, using her Kanohi mask to communicate with the Rahi's lead animal.

In her time as a Toa Hordika, Nokama discovered a bo with nature she had not known before. After Vakam betrayal of the group, Nokama took over as team lead and led the successful search for the Rahi Keetongu and t successful attack on the Visorak.

As a Turaga, Nokama led the village of Ga-Koro on t island of Mata Nui. She gained a reputation for decidi issues based on logic, rather than emotion, and listening every side carefully before making a decision.

During her time as a Toa Metru, Nokama wore the Kanc Rau, the Great Mask of Translation, and carried tv hydroblades.

ONEWA

Onewa was a Po-Matoran carver in Metru Nui when he became the Toa Metru of Stone. From the start, he was skeptical of Vakama's leadership and quick to insult the Toa of Fire. He could be impatient and temperamental and often seemed to expect the worst. It was only with great effort that he and Vakama were able to work together to find the Great Disks and defeat the Morbuzakh. During the battle with Makuta Teridax, Onewa discovered the power of his Great Mask of Mind Control and used it to help stop Nidhiki and Krekka.

After that battle was won, and the Toa had begun their journey to Mata Nui, Onewa had a strange experience. He stumbled upon a bizarre creature hidden in a vault, which attached itself to his mask and made contact with his mind. Onewa saw visions of things to come, including the attack on Metru Nui by the Visorak horde. (It would later be revealed that this creature and others like it were created by the mysterious organization known as the Order of Mata Nui.)

After becoming a Toa Hordika, Onewa found it hard to control his rage. Still, it was he who helped to convince Krahka to ally with the Toa against the Visorak. This proved an important turning point in the struggle against the spiders.

As a Turaga, Onewa learned from his past mistakes and turned into a fine leader of the village of Po-Koro. He was nicknamed "the referee" because he always tried to resolve any arguments among villagers fairly. Along with Whenua, he invented the sport of kolhii, which became the most popular game on the island of Mata Nui. Later, he would strongly oppose revealing all that had happened on Metru Nui to the Matoran and the Toa Nuva and Vakama had to do it over his objections.

As a Toa Metru, Onewa wore the Kanohi Komau, the Mask of Mind Control, and carried twin proto pitons.

WHEN I LAUNCHED MY PLAN TO TAKE OVER THIS UNIVERSE, I WILL ADMIT THAT I DID NOT THINK BIG ENOUGH. I THOUGHT I COULD BE SATISFIED WITH SEIZING POWER IN THE CITY OF METRU NUI. BY DOING THAT, I COULD CONTROL THE FLOW OF ENERGY FROM THE CITY'S POWER PLANTS TO THE REST OF THE UNIVERSE NOT TO MENTION BEING ABLE TO DECIDE WHEN – OR IF – THE GREAT SPIRIT WOULD EVER AWAKEN AGAIN.

NOW, AS I LOOK BACK AT MY SETBACKS THERE, I REALIZE IT WAS FATE'S WAY OF TELLING ME I WAS MEANT TO RULE MORE THAN JUST ONE CITY. OH, THE PLAN BEGAN WELL ENOUGH – I CAPTURED AND IMPRISONED METRU NUI'S PATHETIC RULER, TURAGA DUME, AND TOOK HIS PLACE. I REPROGRAMMED THE ROBOT GUARDIANS OF THE CITY, THE VAHKI, TO SERVE ME. I HIRED DARK HUNTERS TO ELIMINATE TOA LHIKAN AND HIS TEAMMATES. AND I FOUND A FOOLISH LITTLE MASK MAKER, VAKAMA, AND DEMANDED HE CREATE FOR ME A MASK OF TIME.

I WAS LIKE A VISORAK SPIDER IN THE CENTER OF ITS WEB, WATCHING AS MY PREY BECAME ENTANGLED IN THE STRANDS. ONE BY ONE, TOA WERE MADE TO DISAPPEAR, UNTIL ONLY LHIKAN REMAINED. THE MATORAN OF THE CITY ACCEPTED ME AS DUME, NEVER ONCE QUESTIONING MY ORDER TO CLOSE THE SEA GATES AND ISOLATE METRU NUI FROM THE REST OF THE UNIVERSE.

IF THERE WAS A MOMENT WHEN IT BEGAN TO GO WRONG, IT WAS WHEN NIDHIKI AND KREKKA FAILED TO PREVENT LHIKAN FROM HANDING OUT TOA STONES TO SIX WORTHLESS MATORAN. THOSE SIX BECAME THE TOA METRU, A NEW TEAM OF MEDDLERS DETERMINED TO INTERFERE WITH MY PLANS. I HAD UNLEASHED AN INTELLIGENT PLANT MENACE OF MY OWN CREATION, THE MORBUZAKH, ON THE CITY DRIVING THE MATORAN INTO PANIC. THE TOA METRU USED THE GREAT DISKS AND DESTROYED IT.

BUT EVEN THAT I WAS ABLE TO USE TO MY ADVANTAGE. THEY HAD TEMPORARILY USED UP THEIR ELEMENTAL POWERS IN THE FIGHT AND HAD NOT YET MASTERED THEIR MASK POWERS. WHEN THEY COULDN'T SHOW EITHER TO A CROWD OF ASSEMBLED VILLAGERS, I BRANDED THEM AS FRAUDS AND ORDERED THEIR ARREST. BUT MY VAHKI AND DARK HUNTERS WERE ONLY ABLE TO CAPTURE THREE LEAVING VAKAMA, NOKAMA, AND MATAU FREE.

WOULD NOT ALLOW ANY DELAY IN MY PLANS.
HILE SOME VAHKI PURSUED THE THREE TOA, THE
ST CAPTURED THE CITY'S MATORAN AND PUT
EM INTO CANISTERS WHERE THEY WOULD BE
RCED INTO A DEEP SLEEP. OVER TIME, THEY
OULD LOSE THEIR MEMORIES OF HOW THEY HAD
EN IMPRISONED. THEN I WOULD FREE THEM
ND THEY WOULD HAIL ME AS THEIR RESCUER,
ADLY GIVING ME THEIR LOYALTY AND COMPLETE
NTROL OF METRU NUI. OF COURSE, IT WOULD
KE MANY CENTURIES FOR THAT TO HAPPEN...
LESS I HAD THE KANOHI VAHI, THE MASK OF
ME, AND COULD SPEED TIME UP FOR THE
EEPING MATORAN.

KAMA HAD SUCCEEDED IN MAKING THE MASK,
COMBINING THE SIX GREAT DISKS. BUT BEFORE
E VAHKI COULD GET IT AWAY FROM HIM, HE AND
S ALLIES HAD SUCCEEDED IN FREEING THE
HER THREE TOA METRU AND LHIKAN, WHO HAD
OW BECOME A TURAGA. THEN THEY DARED TO
OUNT AN ATTACK ON ME - ME! - TOTALLY
NORING HOW HOPELESS THEIR CAUSE MUST BE.

EDING MORE POWER FOR THE COMING FIGHT,
ABSORBED THE ENERGIES OF THE METRU NUI
WER PLANT, ALONG WITH THE BODIES AND
NDS OF NIDHIKI, KREKKA, AND MY FLYING RAHI,
VAWK. SHAPESHIFTING INTO A LARGE, WINGED
RM, I CHALLENGED VAKAMA FOR POSSESSION
THE VAHI, EVEN AS EARTHQUAKES CRUMBLED
E CITY AROUND US. HE WAS TRICKY, DUCKING
D DODGING AND HIDING FROM MY SIGHT UNTIL
S FRIENDS COULD ARRIVE.

EN THEN, I WOULD HAVE ABSORBED HIM AS
AD THE DARK HUNTERS HAD HE NOT SUDDENLY
ALIZED HOW TO USE THE MASK OF TIME.
SLOWED TIME DOWN AROUND ME, DELAYING
REVENGE. BUT THE FOOL COULD NOT CONTROL
E VAHI'S POWER AND TRAPPED HIMSELF IN THE
ME SLOWDOWN AS WELL. I KNEW I HAD ONLY TO
IT UNTIL HIS WILL WEAKENED AND HE WOULD
MINE.

NEVER SAW TURAGA LHIKAN RUNNING TOWARD
, OR HIS LEAP IN BETWEEN US. BUT WHEN TIME
LAST FLOWED NORMALLY, IT WAS LHIKAN WHO
OK THE BLAST MEANT FOR VAKAMA AND DIED.
VEN A SECOND CHANCE AT LIFE, THE TOA METRU
TACKED, TRAPPING ME INSIDE A PRISON OF
LID PROTODERMIS LOCKED WITH A TOA SEAL.

EY THOUGHT ME DEFEATED AND HELPLESS, OF
OURSE... TOA OFTEN MAKE THAT MISTAKE. THEY
OULD NOT KNOW THAT I WAS REACHING OUT
TH MY MIND TO A PAIR OF MY SERVANTS, WHO
OULD SOON ARRIVE IN METRU NUI AND AVENGE
Y DEFEAT...

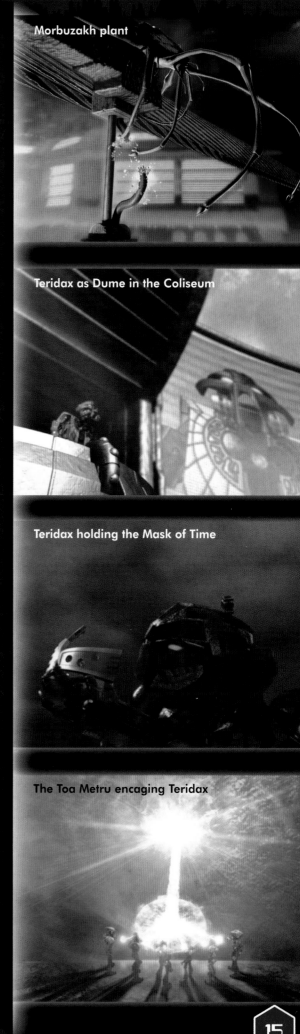

Morbuzakh plant

Teridax as Dume in the Coliseum

Teridax holding the Mask of Time

The Toa Metru encaging Teridax

The Visorak

TOA HORDIKA
AND THE VISORAK INVASION

In the tens of thousands of years before the Brotherhood of Makuta rebelled against Mata Nui, they often employed Toa as guards. One such Toa team was the Toa Hagah, led by a brave hero named Norik. When the Hagah discovered that the Brotherhood had raided the island of Artakha, stolen the Mask of Light from that place, and were raising an army of Visorak for war, they knew what they had to do.

The Toa Metru trapped by the Visorak

Norik led his team on a raid on the Makuta fortress at Destral and stole the mask back. But their escape was not without a price – Makuta's lieutenant, Roodaka, used her power to mutate them into small, half-bestial beings called Rahaga. Despite this, the Rahaga managed to escape to Metru Nui with the Mask of Light.

Roodaka and Toa Hordika Vakama

Many years passed, during which time Rahaga stayed hidden in the Archives. T Makuta Teridax tried and failed to seize po in Metru Nui and was imprisoned by the Metru. The heroes left the city to seek out a land for the Matoran to settle in. While were gone, disaster struck. An army of Viso led by Brotherhood of Makuta servants Sid and Roodaka, attacked and conquered the Rahi were captured and transformed mutant beasts by Visorak venom. Those V who still survived were destroyed by the Vis as well, leaving the city defenseless.

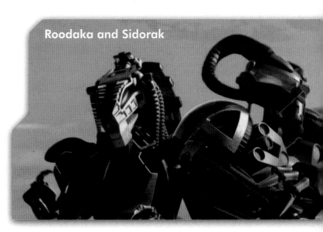

Roodaka and Sidorak

When the Toa Metru returned to collect the sleeping Matoran, they were ambus Visorak venom turned them into animal- Toa Hordika and they were about to be ki when they were rescued by the Rahaga. learned that the only possible cure for condition was a legendary Rahi beast know Keetongu, one some of the Rahaga belie was hidden somewhere in Metru Nui.

The Toa Hord

The Toa Hordika launched a search Keetongu even as they fought the Viso throughout the city. In their darkest mom Vakama abandoned the team, allied Sidorak and Roodaka, and captured all but of the Rahaga. It seemed as if the city doomed.

Roodaka arriving at the Coliseum

ut all was not yet lost. Allying with Krahka nd a mighty creature, the Tahtorak, the Toa ored a victory against the Visorak. scovering the location of Keetongu resulted yet another powerful ally. In the final ssault on the Visorak's headquarters in the oliseum, Matau managed to convince akama to fight alongside the Toa once more. oodaka betrayed Sidorak, leaving him to be lled by Keetongu. Vakama used his control ver the Visorak (gained while he was on eir side) to order the army to abandon the y.

Keetongu

hat left only Roodaka. She battled the Toa etru, baiting them into striking at her with eir elemental powers. The Toa Hordika did ot realize that she carried a portion of the ge in which they had captured Makuta. By riking it with their powers, they were ndoing the Toa seal and freeing Teridax. The akuta rescued Roodaka from death at the st moment.

The Rahaga

The Toa Hordika knew they had to move fast. Cured by Keetongu and returned to being Toa Metru, they gathered the sleeping Matoran into airships for transport to the island of Mata Nui. The Rahaga, Keetongu and Turaga Dume chose to stay behind and look after the city.

The Toa Hordika asking Keetongu for help

Vakama returned once more to Metru Nui, in search of the Kanohi Vahi, which had been lost in the fight. His adventure forced him into an alliance with Teridax, as both tried to stop The Shadowed One from claiming both the mask and the city. In the end, The Shadowed One was defeated. Vakama forced Teridax to promise to leave the island of Mata Nui alone for one full year by threatening to destroy the Vahi and rip time itself to pieces.

The Toa Metru awakening the Matoran

Together again on the island of Mata Nui, the Toa Metru used their power to awaken the sleeping Matoran. In doing so, they transformed into Turaga. The Matoran were safe once more, though far from home, with no Toa to protect them. And it would only be a matter of time before Makuta Teridax would strike again...

THE ISLAND OF MATA NUI

The city of Metru Nui rests inside a huge dome, and the place that came to be called "Mata Nui" is on the outer surface of that dome, surrounded by a vast ocean. It was discovered by the Toa Metru shortly after their defeat of Teridax. Wild and untamed, but beautiful as well, it was considered a place where the Matoran could live in peace and safety. The Toa Metru named it Mata Nui after the Great Spirit. Following their battles with the Visorak, the Toa brought the population of Metru Nui here. (Due to the effects of the canisters they had been imprisoned in, the Matoran gradually lost their memories of Metru Nui and came to believe that they had always lived on Mata Nui.)

Originally, the island was completely barren. During the terrible earthquakes triggered by Makuta, a leak of a powerful substance called energized protodermis caused incredibly rapid plant growth. By the time the Toa arrived there for the first time, there were great jungles and more on what had once been nothing but rock.

The island of Mata Nui is 486 kilometers long and 285 kilometers wide. It is divided into six major regions, or "wahi":

- **Ta-Wahi:** A hot, volcanic area, noted for its lava falls and rivers of molten magma. Site of the village of Ta-Koro.
- **Po-Wahi:** A barren, rocky wasteland in the northern section of the island. Site of village of Po-Koro.
- **Ko-Wahi:** A cold, icy land, known for its many snowfalls and avalanches. It was the site of the village of Ko-Koro and the island's highest point, Mount Ihu (named by Nuju after a deceased Matoran friend of his from Metru Nui).
- **Ga-Wahi:** A watery area, home to Naho Bay and numerous species of marine life. Site of the village of Ga-Koro, which was built on top of large lily pads.
- **Le-Wahi:** A marshy land known for its thick jungle and treacherous Fau Swamp. Site of the village of Le-Koro.
- **Onu-Wahi:** A largely barren region in the northwestern section of the island. Although the area appeared uninhabited, the thriving village of Onu-Koro could be found underground here.

Each region also contained a small temple, or "kini," dedicated to the Toa the Matoran were sure would someday come to help them.

Shortly after their arrival, the Matoran and Turaga used parts of the airships that had brought them there along with natural resources to build the villages. In the first year, it was possible for Matoran to easily travel from region to region. Later, Makuta Teridax's control of the island's wildlife would make travel overland too dangerous. As a result, the villages were largely isolated and the differences in their societies became more obvious.

The team of Toa destined to one day reawaken the Great Spirit arrived on the shores of Mata Nui in Toa canisters. Led by Tahu, they would be named the "Toa Mata" by the Matoran inhabitants. Along with battling Rahi beasts, these Toa would challenge the Bohrok, Bohrok-Kal, evil Rahkshi and Makuta Teridax himself during their year on the island.

Metru Nui could be reached from Mata Nui through a series of underground tunnels. Later, it would be discovered that these tunnels were intended for use by the insectoid Bohrok.

ONU-KORO

Located beneath the surfac Onu-Wahi, Onu-Koro was village of Earth and home t Onu-Matoran. Made up of tu and caves, Onu-Koro was k for its protodermis mines Ussal crab races. It was defe by the Ussalry, Matoran mou on top of the large c Onu-Koro was damaged flood caused by the Bohrok later destroyed by the Rahksh

GA-KORO

Floating atop of the waters o northeastern coast of Mata Ga-Koro was the village of V and home to the Ga-Mate Travel to and from the main is was by canoe, but whirlp and strong currents made dangerous trip. The dwe places of the Matoran were r out of seaweed. The village largely rebuilt and redesi following a Bohrok attack.

KO-KORO

Hidden beneath a massive block that separates two gla Ko-Koro was the village of Ice home to the Ko-Matoran. Ko- was surrounded by crevasses that were big enou swallow even a large Villagers lived either in cav inside the glaciers or in huts r of ice. Defense was provided group of Matoran called Sanctum Guard. Ko-Koro later heavily damaged b Rahkshi attack.

LE-KORO

Built in the treetops above the Swamp, Le-Koro was the villa Air and home to the Le-Mata These Matoran spent mos their time among the tree and vines, chattering to other in a dialect of their called "treespeak." Le-Koro defended by Matoran ri Gukko birds. The village badly damaged by the Bohro later rebuilt.

PO-KORO

Located in the Motara desert, Po-Koro was the village of Stone and home to the Po-Matoran. A harsh climate, featuring intense heat and sandstorms, kept most outsiders away. Villagers lived in stone huts and caves. Protection of the village was provided by a small group of Matoran known as the Po-Koro Guard, who rode on flightless desert birds called dikapi.

TA-KORO

Located in the Lake of Fire, near the great Mangai volcano, this was the village of Fire and home to the Ta-Matoran. Villagers lived in homes made of cooled magma, with heat provided by a small lava stream that flowed through the village. It was defended by the Ta-Koro Guard, led by Jaller. It was also home to the largest kolhii stadium on Mata Nui. Ta-Koro was destroyed by the Rahkshi.

MANGAI

The great volcano of Mata Nui, located in Ta-Wahi. Shortly after their arrival on Mata Nui, Toa Lewa and Toa Onua combined to stop a massive eruption of the volcano triggered by Teridax. It was later discovered that the lava coming out of the volcano was actually molten protodermis from Ta-Metru in Metru Nui.

KINI-NUI

This large temple, dedicated to the Great Spirit Mata Nui, was long a site for meditation and contemplation. It was partially built by the Great Beings and completed by the Turaga and Matoran after their arrival on Mata Nui. A group of Matoran known as the Chronicler's Company defended the site from Rahi attack. It was also the location of the first appearance of the Rahkshi on the island.

MANGAIA

Located beneath Kini-Nui, this was one of many lairs that Makuta Teridax had in the area. It was from here that he directed his Rahi and Rahkshi attacks against the Matoran. It was also the site of his battle with Takanuva, Toa of Light. Metru Nui could be reached by raising an incredibly heavy stone door in Mangaia.

19

TAHU

Toa Mata of Fire, Tahu was made leader of the team by the Orde
Mata Nui. After extensive training, he took the team to Karda Nui wh
they battled the intelligent lightning bolts called Avohkah. Knowing
Toa would have to remain in the Codrex until the day they would
needed to aid Mata Nui, Tahu tricked his team into entering just as
energy storm made it impossible to escape the area.

Like the other Toa, Tahu's memories were badly confused when
arrived on the island of Mata Nui. His instincts led to him becom
leader of the team there as well, but he frequently clashed with Kopa
who objected to Tahu's recklessness and impatient nature. His tende
to act without planning first led him into some very danger
situations, including being trapped in a Bohrok nest. Still, no one co
question his bravery or his commitment to their mission.

As a Toa Mata, Tahu wore the Kanohi Hau, the Mask of Shielding, and carried a fire sword. Tahu mer
with Toa Onua and Toa Pohatu to form Toa Kaita Akamai during the first battle with Makuta Terida

GALI

Toa Mata of Water, Gali brought patience and compassion to the
team. Often, she was the only one who held the group together,
frequently intervening in fights between Tahu and Kopaka. When
she first arrived in Ga-Wahi, she saved the village of Ga-Koro from
a rampaging Tarakava, immediately earning the respect and trust
of the villagers. She was always willing to spend time with the
Ga-Matoran, teaching and learning.

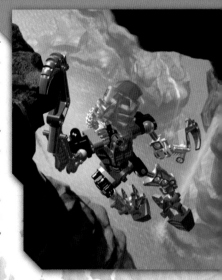

During a battle with Rahi, Gali struck her head on a rock. While
unconscious, she had a vision of two powerful Toa, Akamai and
Wairuha. They told her that they would be formed by her and her
friends. Later, she, Toa Lewa, and Toa Kopaka would merge to form
Wairuha during a battle with the forces of Makuta Teridax.

Gali was happiest in the water and excelled at swimming and diving. As a Toa Mata, she wore the Kan
Kaukau, the Mask of Water Breathing, and carried two hooks that allowed her to scale slippery surfa

COMING OF THE TOA MATA

When the Great Spirit fell asleep, the Toa Mata's canisters were automatically launched from the Coo
in Karda Nui. But something went wrong. Instead of landing in the ocean outside of the domes
immediately making landfall on the island of Mata Nui, they remained floating in the water for 1
years with the Toa sleeping inside.

Unaware the Toa were out there, the Matoran struggled to survive the Rahi attacks sparked by Teric
One Matoran, Takua, journeyed across the island to retrieve tools stolen from the Turaga of the
villages as well as Toa stones. These were rocks with a small portion of Toa power in them, designe
spark the transformation of Matoran into new Toa.

Takua collected all six stones and placed them around Kini-Nui. When he was done, a beam of ene
suddenly shot from them, sending Takua flying into the sky. He crashed on the beach of Ta-We
unharmed but with amnesia. He had no way of knowing that the beam of energy had sent a signc
the Toa Mata's canisters, causing them to travel to shore and open to reveal the Toa inside.

After a millennium, the Toa Mata had finally arrived on Mata Nui. But they all had badly dama
memories and no idea of where they were or what they were supposed to do. But Makuta Teri
guessed who they were and what their mission might be and set out to test their power

KOPAKA

The Toa Mata of Ice, Kopaka was the least friendly of all the heroes, preferring to work alone. He had little patience for fools and reckless behavior and frequently argued with Tahu (and sometimes Lewa). Kopaka often felt the team would be better off if he was the leader, and it was only Gali who kept the Toa of Ice and the Toa of Fire from coming to blows. Kopaka believed in studying an enemy and learning its weaknesses, rather than just charging into battle. It was he who discovered the attacking Bohrok were not aliens, but actually came from beneath the island itself. Although he was brilliant and brave, Kopaka's cold attitude and sharp words sometimes got on his teammates' nerves.

He regarded Gali and Pohatu as friends, but rarely showed any affection. Still, his power saved the lives of the team more than once, including the time he actually froze a molten lava flow before it could engulf them.

As a Toa Mata, Kopaka wore the Kanohi Akaku, the Mask of X-Ray Vision, and carried an ice sword and shield.

POHATU

Easygoing and friendly, Pohatu, the Toa of Stone, was also the strongest of the Toa Mata. His preferred method of attack was to use his powerful legs to kick boulders at an opponent, a skill he displayed early in his time on Mata Nui when Po-Koro was under attack by venom-spitting rock worms. Knowing that getting too close to the creatures would mean certain defeat, Pohatu ricocheted boulders off multiple cliff walls and downed dozens of the beasts at once.

In a team of strong personalities, Pohatu made a point of trying to get along with everyone. He knew that sometimes even Toa who didn't want any help, like Kopaka, still needed some. Pohatu learned not to take "no" for an answer and to use his sense of humor to keep fights from breaking out among the others.

As a Toa Mata, Pohatu wore the Kanohi Kakama, the Mask of Speed. He did not carry a weapon.

THE SEARCH FOR THE MASKS

1. 2. 3. 4. 5. 6.

When the Toa Metru arrived on Mata Nui, they brought with them Masks of Power called Kanohi. These masks they hid all over the island, in places that only a true Toa would be able to reach. As Turaga, they told the newly arrived Toa Mata that they had to seek out and retrieve these masks.

Each Toa had to have one of each of these masks when they were done:

Kanohi Kakama, the Mask of Speed
Kanohi Miru, the Mask of Levitation
Kanohi Akaku, the Mask of X-Ray Vision
Kanohi Kaukau, the Mask of Water Breathing
Kanohi Hau, the Mask of Shielding
Kanohi Pakari, the Mask of Strength

The masks were concealed everywhere from the depths of the ocean to the tops of mountain peaks. In many cases, the locations were guarded by Rahi sent by Makuta Teridax. Once the Toa had all their masks, they brought them to Kini-Nui and placed them on life-size carvings of themselves. In the next instant, the masks were replaced by new golden Kanohi, each of which contained the powers of all six. The Toa Mata wore these golden masks in their battle with Makuta Teridax.

ONUA

The wisest of the heroes, Onua, the Toa of Earth, was a team mem[ber] others knew they could rely on. Though he never said much, he w[as] always there when he was needed. Twice, he saved Lewa from terri[ble] fates – the first time when the Toa of Air had been forced to wea[r a] mask infected with Makuta's shadow, and the second when the Boh[rok] swarm had taken over his mind with a parasitic krana. In both cas[es,] it was Onua's quiet reassurance and faith in Lewa's strength t[hat] helped the Toa overcome the threat.

If Onua had a flaw, it was that he was too willing to let others m[ake] their own mistakes. He saw no point in arguing with Tahu or Kop[aka] – better, he felt, to let them do what they wished and learn lessons [on] their own. As with all other residents of Onu-Koro, Onua had we[ak] vision in daylight but excellent night vision. A skilled tunneler, he o[nce] saved a dozen Matoran by rapidly digging them a route out o[f a] caved-in mine shaft, defeating a vicious doom viper along the way[.]

As a Toa Mata, Onua wore the Kanohi Pakari, the Mask of Streng[th] and relied on his natural claws as a weapon.

LEWA

For Lewa, Toa of Air, life as a hero was all about adventure and fun. He loved to explore, rarely worried about danger, and considered every threat just another challenge to be overcome. Although all six Toa were the same age, to an outsider, Lewa would have seemed like the youngest. He never took things very seriously. With his ability to glide on the winds, he often said he felt sorry for beings who had to spend their whole lives on the ground, or worse, in the water (Lewa hated the water).

Early on, Lewa had no interest in being part of a team, feeling that he could handle everything on his own. Unfortunately, his reckless, daring nature often led him into trouble. After having his mind taken over by both Makuta Teridax and the Bohrok, Lewa was forced to grow up a bit and realize that being a Toa was not all a game. He had to win back the trust of some of his teammates, especially Tahu, who worried that Lewa might still be under the influence of their enemies.

As a Toa Mata, Lewa wore the Kanohi Miru, the Mask of Levitation, and carried an axe. Extremely agile in the air, he was clumsier on the ground, so he preferred to do battle in the sky or in the treetops.

MATORAN ALPHABET

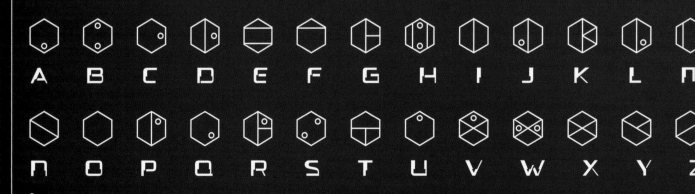

A B C D E F G H I J K L M
N O P Q R S T U V W X Y Z

Manas crabs

FOR ALMOST 1000 YEARS, I ATTACKED THE MATORAN OF MATA NUI WITH WILD RAHI, STORMS, AND PLAGUES, ALL DESIGNED TO BREAK THEIR SPIRITS. JUST WHEN I BELIEVED THEY MIGHT BE READY TO CRACK, THE TOA MATA ARRIVED, TO GIVE THEM NEW HOPE. OR WERE THEY REALLY THE TOA MATA? I HAD TO FIND OUT, AND SO SET RAHI AGAINST THEM, KNOWING TRUE TOA WOULD BE ABLE TO DEFEAT THEM WITH EASE.

THAT THEY DID, BATTLING THEIR WAY EVEN PAST THE MANAS CRABS WHO GUARDED MY LAIR AND THE SHADOW TOA I UNLEASHED UPON THEM. WHEN THEY REACHED MANGAIA, I WARNED THEM OF THE POWER THEY FACED, BUT THEY WOULD NOT SURRENDER. INSTEAD, THEY ATTACKED. UNWILLING TO WASTE MY ENERGIES IN BATTLE WITH THEM, I LET THEM BELIEVE THEY HAD BEATEN ME. BUT EVEN AS THEY DEPARTED, SECURE IN THEIR VICTORY, I WAS PLOTTING TO STRIKE AGAIN.

A SIMPLE SONIC SIGNAL AWAKENED THE BOHROK, CREATIONS OF THE GREAT BEINGS WHOSE MISSION WAS TO SCOUR CLEAN THE ISLAND OF MATA NUI (FOR REASONS NOT EVEN I UNDERSTOOD AT THE TIME). IN THE TENS OF THOUSANDS, THEY SWARMED ACROSS THE ISLAND. MOUNTAINS CRUMBLED, FORESTS FELL, RIVERS TURNED TO DUST BEFORE THEM. THE TOA MATA WERE OVERWHELMED, TRYING TO FIGHT EVERYWHERE AT ONCE.

OH, THE "HEROES" HAD THEIR SUCCESSES, SUCH AS DISCOVERING HOW HELPLESS THE BOHROK WERE WITHOUT THE KRANA, SMALL CREATURES THAT CONTROLLED THEM. THEY WERE WISE ENOUGH TO IGNORE THE SWARMS AND STRIKE AT THE TWO BAHRAG, QUEENS OF THE BOHROK, WHO LIVED BELOW GROUND. WHILE THE MATORAN BATTLED THE BOHROK ABOVE USING THEIR OWN MECHANICAL CREATIONS, THE TOA MATA MADE USE OF ARMORED EXO-TOA SUITS THEY HAD FOUND IN THE BAHRAG CHAMBER.

THE BAHRAG, OF COURSE, NEVER HAD A CHANCE – ONLY A FOOL WOULD HAVE THOUGHT THEY COULD DEFEAT SIX TOA. BUT THEY HAD ACHIEVED WHAT I WISHED, BY DELAYING AND EXHAUSTING THE TOA. MY VICTORY WAS NOT COMPLETE, HOWEVER – SHORTLY AFTER DEFEATING THE BAHRAG, THE TOA FELL INTO TUBES OF ENERGIZED PROTODERMIS. THAT STRANGE SUBSTANCE TRANSFORMED THE TOA, GIVING THEM NEW MASKS, NEW WEAPONS AND ARMOR, AND GREATER POWER THAN BEFORE.

THEY CALLED THEMSELVES THE "TOA NUVA"... AND THEY WERE ABOUT TO FIND OUT THAT POWER CAN BE A CURSE... AND THE LOSS OF IT EVEN WORSE.

...nok swarm

Toa Gali fighting the Gahlok

Exo-Tahu fighting Cahdok

THE BOHROK

Bohrok are insect-like mechanical beings, controlled by small, organic creatures called krana. They sleep in nests that extend far below the island of Mata Nui, waiting for the signal to hatch. Their mission: "clean" Mata Nui until it has been returned to the barren rock that it once was. The Bohrok are ruled by two swarm queens, the Bahrag, and assisted by small robots called Bohrok Va. Unleashed by Makuta Teridax, their rampage was stopped when the Toa Nuva defeated and imprisoned the Bahrag. (It was later discovered that many Matoran of Light evolve into Bohrok at a certain point of their lives, changing from bio-mechanical beings to completely mechanical ones and losing their individual wills.)

There are six types of Bohrok:

TAHNOK
Bohrok of Fire, whose shields could melt any substance. Tahnok were the most aggressive and unpredictable of the six breeds. They attacked both Ta-Koro and Po-Koro during the conflict.

GAHLOK
Bohrok of Water, whose shields could draw moisture from any source and direct it at an opponent. Sly and tricky, they never reacted to an attack the same way twice. They were best known for flooding Onu-Koro.

LEHVAK
Bohrok of Acid, whose shields sprayed an acid that could dissolve anything. Lehvak normally operated in small groups and rarely worked with other Bohrok. They were responsible for the destruction of Le-Koro.

PAHRAK
Bohrok of Stone, whose shields could cause violent earthquakes. Brutal and tough, the Pahrak came close to destroying Ga-Koro twice, stopped the first time by a pair of brave Ga-Matoran and the second by the defeat of the Bahrag.

KOHRAK
Bohrok of Ice, whose shields could freeze anything, even an open flame. The intense cold given off by the Kohrak's bodies kept even other Bohrok away from them. The Kohrak were part of the first attacks on Ta-Koro.

NUHVOK
Bohrok of Earth, whose shields could be used to weaken structures from below, causing them to collapse. The Nuhvok were excellent tunnelers but had poor vision in daylight. They assisted the Lehvak in the attack on Le-Koro.

LEWA [NU]

"I am a Toa-hero, here to save you from... whatever it is you need saving from."

LEWA NUVA

When Lewa transformed into a Toa Nuva, he believe[d] had enough power that he did not need the rest o[f the] team. He supported the decision by Tahu and Kopa[ka to] break up the Nuva. But when the Toa Nuva later lost [their] elemental powers, he was forced to team with Tahu [Nuva] to search for Kanohi Nuva masks.

Lewa later saved two Matoran, Takua and Jaller, fro[m a] wild ash bear, and then teamed with the other Toa [Nuva] to battle the Rahkshi. Together with Tahu, he succee[ded] in trapping three of those monstrous creatures in a p[ool] of glass.

As a Toa Nuva, Lewa wore a Nuva version of the [Miru] which allowed him to share his levitation power [with] others nearby. He carried two air katana which dou[bled] as glider wings.

KOPAKA [NUVA]

"The evil on [this] island is abo[ut to] learn that jus[t they] can be very cold."

KOPAKA NUVA

Turning into Toa Nuva seemed to bring out the wor[st in] Kopaka and Tahu, who immediately argued and dec[ided] to break up the team. Kopaka went off on his own [and] the sudden loss of his elemental powers almost cost [him] his life (only Turaga Nuju's use of the Mask of Teleki[nesis] saved him). Against his will, he ended up teamed [with] Pohatu in the search for Kanohi Nuva masks. Po[hatu] almost died on the adventure, and the two woun[d up] closer friends in the end.

Later, Kopaka saved Takua and Jaller from a Rah[kshi] attack, but had to bid them farewell when he saw tha[t the] village of Ko-Koro had been badly damaged. He fo[ught] side by side with the other Toa Nuva, helping to de[feat] the rest of the Rahkshi.

As a Toa Nuva, Kopaka wore a Nuva version of the A[kaku] and was able to share its X-ray vision powers with oth[ers]. He carried an ice blade that could be split in two and [used] as skates.

THE BAHRAG

The Bahrag were twin queens of the Bohrok swarms. Created by the Great Beings, their job was to manufacture the krana needed to control the Bohrok. The two Bahrag, Cahdok and Gahdok, had a mental link to the krana, which enabled them to make sure the Bohrok carried out their mission and could respond to any threat. The Bahrag were also served by robotic creations called the Bohrok Va.

Shortly after they came into being, the Bahrag realized there might come a day when natural disaster or some other event might make it impossible for them to contact the Bohrok. To prepare for this, they mutated six Bohrok into powerful Bohrok-Kal, whose krana-kal were capable of functioning independently of the Bahrag. They would be activated if ever the Bahrag lost touch with the Bohrok. Their mission would be to seek out and rescue the Bahrag.

The Bahrag were not evil creatures. Their mission, to cleanse the island of Mata Nui, was the will of the Great Spirit. But the Bohrok were never meant to be unleashed when anyone was living on the island. The Bahrag did not realize Teridax had sent the signal early, so they saw the Toa's opposition to the Bohrok as a crime.

The Bahrag possessed all the powers of the Bohrok as well as the power to create illusions. They gained strength from being close to each other, but weakened if they were too far apart. When Cahdok and Gahdok were right next to each other, an invisible barrier formed around them that could stop even a blast from Exo-Toa armor.

The Bahrag lived in an underground cavern beneath Mata Nui. It was here that they battled the six Toa. At first, the Bahrag were winning. Then the Toa realized the Exo-Toa armor they were wearing was blocking the use of their elemental powers. After shedding the armor, the Toa combined their elemental powers in one blast to form a solid protodermis prison that cut off the Bahrag's mental link to the Bohrok.

The prison was locked with a Nuva cube, a floating object that could only be unlocked with six objects of power. The Bohrok-Kal were released as soon as the Bahrag were imprisoned and began to seek out those symbols. This would lead to a battle with the new Toa Nuva and the eventual destruction of the Bohrok-Kal. The Bahrag remained imprisoned and the Bohrok returned to their nests and went back to sleep, awaiting another signal to awaken.

TAHU NUVA

Although the transformation into a Toa Nuva made Tahu more powerful, it did not help his temper. He argued with Kopaka, which led to the break-up of the team. The lack of unity would prove costly as the Toa Nuva suffered attacks by both the Bohrok-Kal and the Rahkshi. During the first major battle with the Rahkshi, Tahu was poisoned and driven insane. It took the combined efforts of the other five Toa to save him.

Tahu resumed his leadership of the team, rallying them to stop the Rahkshi at Kini-Nui. He would later take the Toa Nuva into Mangaia for a confrontation with Makuta Teridax.

As a Toa Nuva, Tahu wore the Nuva version of the Hau and was able to share its shielding powers with others. He carried twin magma swords.

TAHU 🔲 NUVA

"With or without powers... together or apart ... we are still the Toa Nuva!"

ONUA NUVA

When Tahu and Kopaka began to argue, and Gali fought to keep the team together, Onua stayed silent. This would prove a mistake, as it cost the team its unity and Onua his friendship with Gali. Following the defeat of the Bohrok-Kal, Onua returned to Onu-Koro. He was there when the Rahkshi attacked, losing a battle with Vorahk. Reviving later, Onua led a counterattack which temporarily defeated the Rahkshi but also brought down the ceiling of Onu-Koro. Only Kopaka's appearance saved Onua and Pohatu.

As a Toa Nuva, Onua wore the Nuva version of the Pakari, enabling him to share its great strength with others. He carried twin quake breakers which could double as all-terrain tracks for his feet.

ONUA 🔳 NUVA

"You did not defeat the Toa Nuva. We simply found your company so boring, we chose to take a nap."

THE RAHKSHI

Called the "sons of Makuta," Rahkshi are vicious, evil warriors for the Brotherhood. A Rahkshi consists of a suit of armor with a leech-like creature called a kraata inside. The kraata is a solidified piece of the essence of a Makuta. It acts as the brain and the power source for the Rahkshi armor. Incredibly destructive, Rahkshi are used only when a Makuta does not care if anything is left standing after the attack.

There are 42 known types of Rahkshi, each with a different power. The six listed below are the ones unleashed by Makuta Teridax on the island of Mata Nui to retrieve the Mask of Light. Other types were fought by the Toa Metru in the past. Rahkshi following direct orders from a Makuta are extremely tough to beat. "Wild Rahkshi," acting on their own, react more like Rahi beasts and are a little easier to trick. Rahkshi are created by exposing a kraata to energized protodermis, which transforms it into armor. A second kraata of the same type then crawls into the armor and powers it up.

GUURAHK
This Rahkshi of Disintegration was one of the first to attack the island of Mata Nui and was part of the successful assault on Ta-Koro. It battled Gali Nuva repeatedly and was responsible for trapping Onua, Pohatu, and Turaga Whenua in a cave full of kraata. It was finally defeated through the combined efforts of Lewa Nuva and Tahu Nuva. Its Staff of Disintegration could create a wave of energy that crumbled any object it touched.

PANRAHK
One of the first three Rahkshi unleashed against the Toa Nuva, this Rahkshi of Fragmentation helped destroy Ta-Koro before being frozen in a lake by Kopaka. Rescued by its brothers, it was finally defeated in the battle at Kini-Nui. Its Staff of Fragmentation could cause objects to explode with great force or send explosive energy beams through the air.

LERAHK
This Rahkshi of Poison was part of the attack on Ta-Koro and was responsible for poisoning Tahu Nuva. Later, it used its power to trap Tahu, Gali and Lewa in a rockslide. Defeated by Kopaka, it was rescued and resumed its attacks until finally being beaten at the battle of Kini-Nui. Its Staff of Poison could infect anything with a toxin, from plants to soil to living beings. The Lerahk had to actually touch its target for the poison to be effective.

KURAHK
Rahkshi of Anger, the Kurahk was part of the attack on Onu-Koro which led to the destruction of that village. It was finally defeated by the combined powers of Onua, Tahu and Kopaka during the final fight at Kini-Nui. Its Staff of Anger fires energy which can cause the target to be consumed by rage.

TURAHK
Turahk is the Rahkshi of Fear. It was a key part of the attack on Onu-Koro, using its power to paralyze Pohatu with fear. It was also responsible for the death of Jaller (the Matoran was later brought back to life by Takutanuva). Turahk was defeated by Takanuva, the Toa of Light, who froze the creature of shadow with a blast of light energy. Turahk's Staff of Fear could make any target either run in panic or remain frozen with sheer terror.

VORAHK
Vorahk are Rahkshi of Hunger. During the battle on Mata Nui, it was responsible for the defeats of Onua Nuva and Kopaka Nuva, before finally being beaten itself by those two Toa and Tahu Nuva. Its Staff of Hunger allowed it to drain energy from an opponent and grow stronger itself. The staff had to make actual contact with the target to work.

GALI NUVA

"The Turaga have said all along that we are six who share one destiny. Is this how we honor their wisdom – by splitting apart?"

GALI NUVA

Gali Nuva fought unsuccessfully to keep the To[a] Nuva team together. When the Bohrok-Kal attacke[d] she teamed with Tahu and Kopaka to search f[or] Kanohi Nuva masks, which brought them in[to] conflict with Makuta Teridax and the Rahi Nui.

After the defeat of the Kal, Gali traveled alone [to] Kini-Nui to meditate. She was a witness to th[e] Rahkshi's first appearance on the island. Althoug[h] she rushed to warn Ta-Koro, she was too late. Late[r] she played a key role in saving Tahu Nuva from th[e] Rahkshi's poison.

As a Toa Nuva, Gali wore the Nuva version of th[e] Kaukau, which enabled her to share the ability [to] water breathe with others. She carried twin aqu[a] axes.

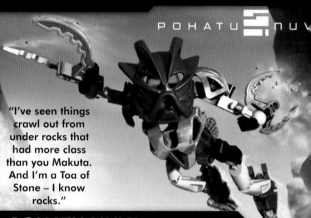

POHATU NUVA

"I've seen things crawl out from under rocks that had more class than you Makuta. And I'm a Toa of Stone - I know rocks."

POHATU NUVA

Pohatu was unhappy about the team's break-u[p] and determined to somehow bring them bac[k] together. He forced his company on Kopaka durin[g] the search for the Kanohi Nuva masks, eve[n] saving the Toa of Ice's life during a rock slide. H[e] later battled the Tahnok-Kal alongside Onua Nuv[a].

Following the defeat of the Kal, Pohatu traveled t[o] Onu-Koro. He was with Onua when the Rahksh[i] Vorahk, Kurahk, and Turahk attacked. Although h[e] suffered a fear attack from Turahk, Pohatu rallied t[o] help temporarily defeat the Rahkshi. He and Onu[a] were then trapped in a cave-in, but rescued b[y] Kopaka.

As a Toa Nuva, Pohatu wore the Nuva version o[f] the Kakama, and was able to share his speed wit[h] others. He carried a pair of climbing claws whic[h] could be used for melee combat or combine[d] together to form a kodan ball.

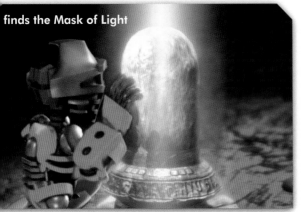
finds the Mask of Light

dies for Takua

uva

TAKUA AND TAKANUVA

As a Matoran living in Ta-Koro, Takua never felt he fit in. He wasn't content to work all day long and never get to travel and see the island. As a result, he often wandered away from his job, until he finally angered Turaga Vakama so much that he was exiled from the village. Takua had a number of adventures, including retrieving the stolen tools of the six Turaga and gathering the Toa stones, which he used to summon the Toa Mata to the island.

What no one knew was that Takua was not a Matoran of Fire at all. He was a Matoran of Light, or Av-Matoran, in disguise. Millennia ago, the Order of Mata Nui had taken Matoran of Light, brainwashed them to forget their identities, and scattered them throughout the universe (including in Metru Nui). It was a safety measure, in case the Brotherhood should ever rebel and try to wipe out the Av-Matoran. All of this took place during a six month period the Order calls the "time slip," the events of which no one but them can remember.

Takua's greatest adventure began when he wandered into a forbidden cavern. There he found a large rock. When he accidentally dropped it into a lava stream, the rock burned away, revealing a golden mask beneath – the Avohkii, or Mask of Light. Bringing it back to Ta-Koro, he was told its discovery meant the Toa of Light would soon arrive. He and his best friend Jaller were sent to find this seventh Toa and give him the mask.

It would not be easy. Makuta Teridax unleashed his evil Rahkshi on the island to hunt down the two Matoran and the Avohkii. Badly frightened, Takua at one point abandoned Jaller to carry on the quest alone. In his heart, Takua knew that he was the one meant to find the Toa of Light, but he feared that the search would lead to disaster.

During a battle with the Rahkshi at Kini-Nui, Jaller took the brunt of a Turahk attack meant for Takua. He died as a result. Realizing now what he had to do, Takua donned the Avohkii. He was instantly transformed from a Matoran into a powerful Toa of Light. His first act was to help defeat the marauding Rahkshi. He then prepared for a confrontation with Makuta Teridax, a final battle for the freedom of all Matoran.

As Takanuva, he wore the Mask of Light, which can project powerful beams of light energy and banish the darkness. It can also bring understanding, turning anger into peace and enemies into allies. Takanuva's control of light allowed him to create everything from blinding flashes to pinpoint laser beams. His power was focused through a Staff of Light which he carried.

MAKUTA'S DIAR

IT WAS NOT LONG AFTER THE TOA NUVA'S TRANSFORMATION THAT SOMETHING MOST
DISTURBING TOOK PLACE. THOUSANDS OF YEARS AGO, THE TOA HAGAH SUCCEEDED IN
STEALING THE MASK OF LIGHT FROM MY FORTRESS AND CONCEALING IT SOMEWHERE.
AS IT TURNED OUT, THE MASK HAD BEEN SMUGGLED TO THE ISLAND OF MATA NUI,
HIDDEN INSIDE A MARKER STONE. A MILLENNIUM LATER, IT WAS FOUND BY
A MISERABLE MATORAN NAMED TAKUA... AND SUDDENLY, FOR THE FIRST TIME, I HAD
REASON TO BE CONCERNED.

I AM A CREATURE OF SHADOW, LIKE MY BROTHER MAKUTA. LIGHT IS OUR ENEMY, AND
THE POSSIBILITY OF A TOA OF LIGHT COMING INTO BEING WAS A CAUSE FOR DREAD.
I HAD RESISTED UNLEASHING RAHKSHI ON MATA NUI, KNOWING THE DESTRUCTION THEY
COULD CAUSE. BUT NOW I HAD NO CHOICE – THE MASK HAD TO BE RECOVERED
BEFORE A TOA OF LIGHT COULD BE CREATED!

MY RAHKSHI DID WHAT THEY DID BEST – DESTROYING, CRUSHING, TERRORIZING, AND
THEY BRUSHED ASIDE TOA NUVA AS IF THE HEROES WERE FIREFLYER BUGS. BUT FOR
ALL THAT, THEY COULD NOT CORNER TAKUA AND HIS FRIEND, JALLER, LONG ENOUGH TO
TAKE BACK THE MASK. EVEN MY EFFORTS TO FILL THE MATORAN WITH FEAR DID NOT
COMPLETELY DETER THEM FROM SEARCHING FOR THE "SEVENTH TOA."

IN THE END... AH, IN THE END, I WAS FORCED TO IMPROVISE. MY RAHKSHI WENT DOWN
IN DISMAL DEFEAT BEFORE A REUNITED TEAM OF TOA NUVA. TAKUA HIMSELF TURNED
OUT TO BE THE DESTINED TOA OF LIGHT, TAKANUVA. WORSE, HE WAS NOT SATISFIED
WITH SURVIVING LONG ENOUGH TO TRANSFORM – HE WAS DETERMINED TO INVADE
MANGAIA AND CHALLENGE ME!

I THOUGHT WITH THE SPEED OF CHAIN LIGHTNING. I KNEW THAT THE MATORAN RE-
TURNING TO METRU NUI WOULD BE THE FIRST STEP TOWARD THE REAWAKENING OF
THE GREAT SPIRIT. BUT I ALSO KNEW THAT INEVITABLY THEY WOULD FIND THE CITY
AGAIN SOMEDAY... AND PERHAPS THE TIME WAS RIGHT FOR THEM TO DO SO. I ALSO
COULD NOT BE CERTAIN THAT I COULD WALK AWAY FROM A BATTLE WITH TAKANUVA
AND HIS ALLIES UNDAMAGED.

THUS WHEN TAKANUVA CONFRONTED ME, I ALLOWED HIM TO THINK HE HAD DEFEATED
ME. I KNEW THAT IF THE TOA BELIEVED ME BEATEN, THEY WOULD MOVE ON, NEVER
IMAGINING WHAT I WAS TRULY PLANNING. OH, ALL DID NOT GO SMOOTHLY... A STUMBLE
INTO ENERGIZED PROTODERMIS RESULTED IN TAKANUVA AND I BEING MERGED INTO
ONE BEING, TAKUTANUVA, A TRULY REVOLTING EXPERIENCE I HOPE NEVER TO REPEAT.
AND WHEN WE RETURNED TO OUR OWN INDIVIDUAL SELVES, A COLLAPSING GATEWAY
SHATTERED MY ARMOR... AN ANNOYING TURN OF EVENTS.

THE MATORAN HAD FOUND THEIR HOME ONCE MORE... THE TOA NUVA WERE TRIUMPHANT... AND THE THREAT OF THE MAKUTA WAS OVER... OR SO I WISHED THEM TO THINK.

FOR A MAKUTA, BEING WITHOUT A BODY IS MOST... DISTURBING. WE EXIST AS ENERGY, BUT STILL WE NEED A SHELL TO INHABIT — IF NOT OUR ARMOR, THEN A ROBOT BODY OR A LIVING FORM WITH NO SPIRIT INSIDE IT (AS DIFFICULT TO FIND AS AN INTELLIGENT TOA). IF WE ARE WITHOUT A BODY FOR MORE THAN FEW WEEKS, WE LOSE THE ABILITY TO KEEP OUR ENERGY INTACT, AND WE DIE.

I HAD BEEN FLOATING IN MANGAIA FOR SOME DAYS IN MY ENERGY STATE, PONDERING MY NEXT MOVE. I HAD SENSED THAT THE GREAT SPIRIT WAS DYING. I KNEW THE TOA WOULD SOON REALIZE THIS AS WELL, AND WOULD SEEK OUT THE LEGENDARY MASK OF LIFE TO SAVE HIM. IF I COULD DELAY THEIR FINDING IT, MY ULTIMATE PLAN COULD STILL SUCCEED. BUT HOW?

THE ANSWER CAME WHEN SIX EX-DARK HUNTERS CALLING THEMSELVES "PIRAKA" CAME TO LOOT MY LAIR. SUBTLY INFLUENCING THEIR MINDS, I IMPLANTED THE IDEA THAT THEY SHOULD JOURNEY TO VOYA NUI, RUMORED HIDING PLACE OF THE MASK OF LIFE. THEY WERE THIEVES BY NATURE, SO IT TOOK LITTLE EFFORT TO CONVINCE THEM TO GO. I ALSO MADE A FEW OTHER "SUGGESTIONS," INCLUDING THE CONSTRUCTION OF A GREAT CRYSTAL VAT TO HOUSE MY ENERGIES ON THE ISLAND.

DID I TRULY BELIEVE THIS COLLECTION OF MISFITS, ROBBERS, AND BRUTES WOULD SUCCEED IN STEALING THE MASK? NO. BUT THEY WOULD FRUSTRATE AND DELAY THE TOA, AND TURN TIME INTO MY ALLY. THEY SUCCESSFULLY INVADED THE ISLAND — POSING AS TOA! — AND USED ZAMOR SPHERES FILLED WITH A SMALL PORTION OF MY SUBSTANCE TO TAKE OVER THE MINDS OF THE MATORAN POPULATION.

THEN THEY BEGAN THEIR SEARCH FOR THE MASK OF LIFE (LOOKING IN THE WRONG PLACE, THE FOOLS), AND STUPIDLY ALLOWING SIX MATORAN TO ESCAPE AND HIDE IN THE MOUNTAINS. THEY MANAGED TO FORGE AN ALLIANCE WITH A WARRIOR NAMED BRUTAKA, ALTHOUGH THERE WAS SOMETHING ABOUT HIM I DID NOT TRUST. BUT WHEN THE TOA NUVA ARRIVED — A SURPRISE TO THE PIRAKA, IF NOT TO ME — THEY OUTDID THEMSELVES. ALTHOUGH IT DID NOT SUIT MY PLANS TO SEE TAHU AND HIS LITTLE BAND KILLED ON VOYA NUI, I WILL ADMIT TO ENJOYING WHAT HAPPENED NEXT...

The Piraka

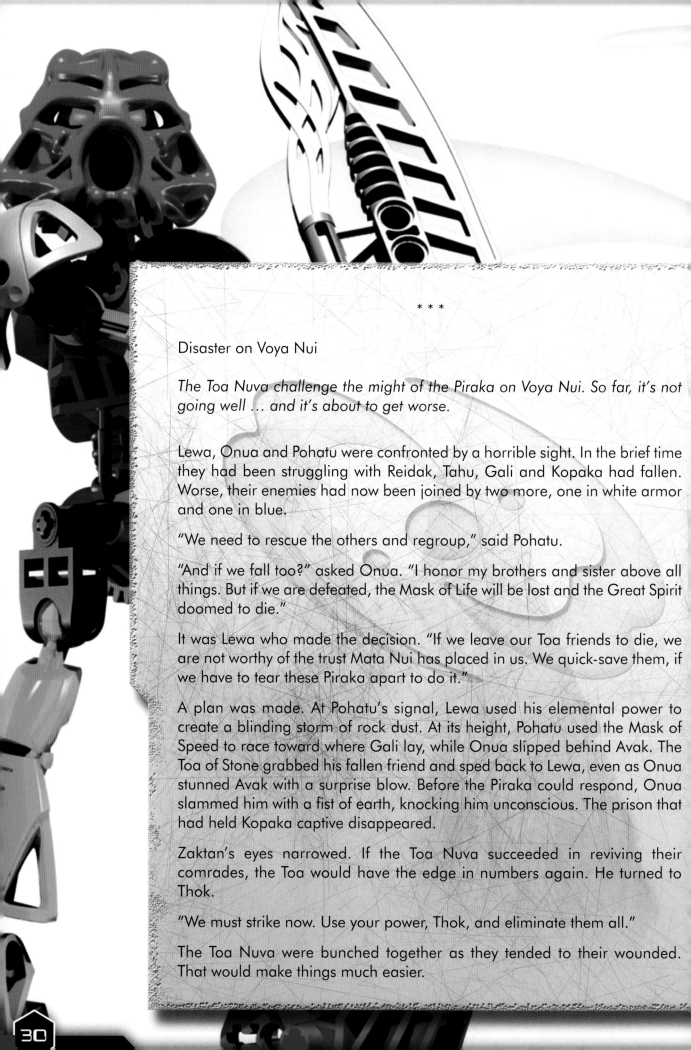

* * *

Disaster on Voya Nui

The Toa Nuva challenge the might of the Piraka on Voya Nui. So far, it's not going well … and it's about to get worse.

Lewa, Onua and Pohatu were confronted by a horrible sight. In the brief time they had been struggling with Reidak, Tahu, Gali and Kopaka had fallen. Worse, their enemies had now been joined by two more, one in white armor and one in blue.

"We need to rescue the others and regroup," said Pohatu.

"And if we fall too?" asked Onua. "I honor my brothers and sister above all things. But if we are defeated, the Mask of Life will be lost and the Great Spirit doomed to die."

It was Lewa who made the decision. "If we leave our Toa friends to die, we are not worthy of the trust Mata Nui has placed in us. We quick-save them, if we have to tear these Piraka apart to do it."

A plan was made. At Pohatu's signal, Lewa used his elemental power to create a blinding storm of rock dust. At its height, Pohatu used the Mask of Speed to race toward where Gali lay, while Onua slipped behind Avak. The Toa of Stone grabbed his fallen friend and sped back to Lewa, even as Onua stunned Avak with a surprise blow. Before the Piraka could respond, Onua slammed him with a fist of earth, knocking him unconscious. The prison that had held Kopaka captive disappeared.

Zaktan's eyes narrowed. If the Toa Nuva succeeded in reviving their comrades, the Toa would have the edge in numbers again. He turned to Thok.

"We must strike now. Use your power, Thok, and eliminate them all."

The Toa Nuva were bunched together as they tended to their wounded. That would make things much easier.

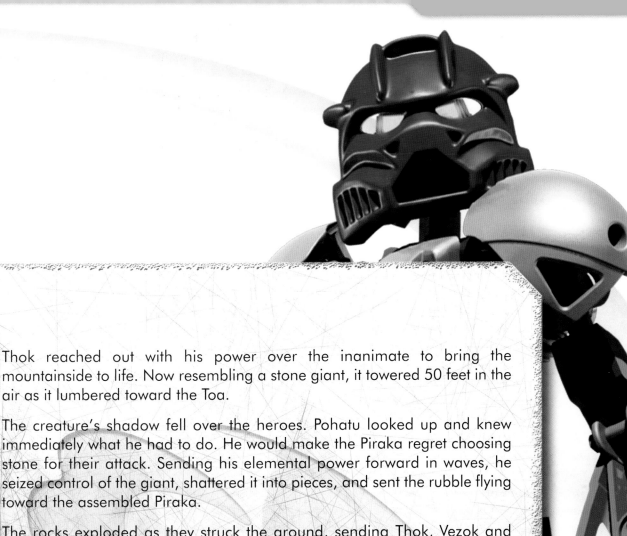

Thok reached out with his power over the inanimate to bring the mountainside to life. Now resembling a stone giant, it towered 50 feet in the air as it lumbered toward the Toa.

The creature's shadow fell over the heroes. Pohatu looked up and knew immediately what he had to do. He would make the Piraka regret choosing stone for their attack. Sending his elemental power forward in waves, he seized control of the giant, shattered it into pieces, and sent the rubble flying toward the assembled Piraka.

The rocks exploded as they struck the ground, sending Thok, Vezok and Zaktan scrambling for cover. Hakann chose that moment to strike, blasting Pohatu and Lewa with mental energy and felling them both. That left only Onua still at full strength.

The Toa of Earth stood among the bodies of his friends. He remembered his own words – wasn't retrieving the Mask of Life what was most important? Should he try to escape to fight another day? Then he looked at his fellow Toa, unconscious, perhaps dead. These were friends he had fought beside, laughed with, mourned with, now helpless at the hands of their enemies. In that moment, Onua made his decision – he would live or die here as a Toa Nuva.

Ripping a half ton of rock free from the ground, Onua hurled it at Zaktan. Before it had even struck home, Onua was running toward his foes, a chilling battle cry escaping from his mouth.

He never made it. The powers of Zaktan, Thok and Hakann struck at him at once, slowing him down but not stopping him. It was left to Vezok to strike the final blow, smashing the Toa of Earth into oblivion.

"They're still alive," reported Vezok, looking at the Toa lying strewn about the battlefield. "Even the one I hit."

"Do you want me to cage them?" asked Avak. "Maybe they have information on the Mask of Life we can use."

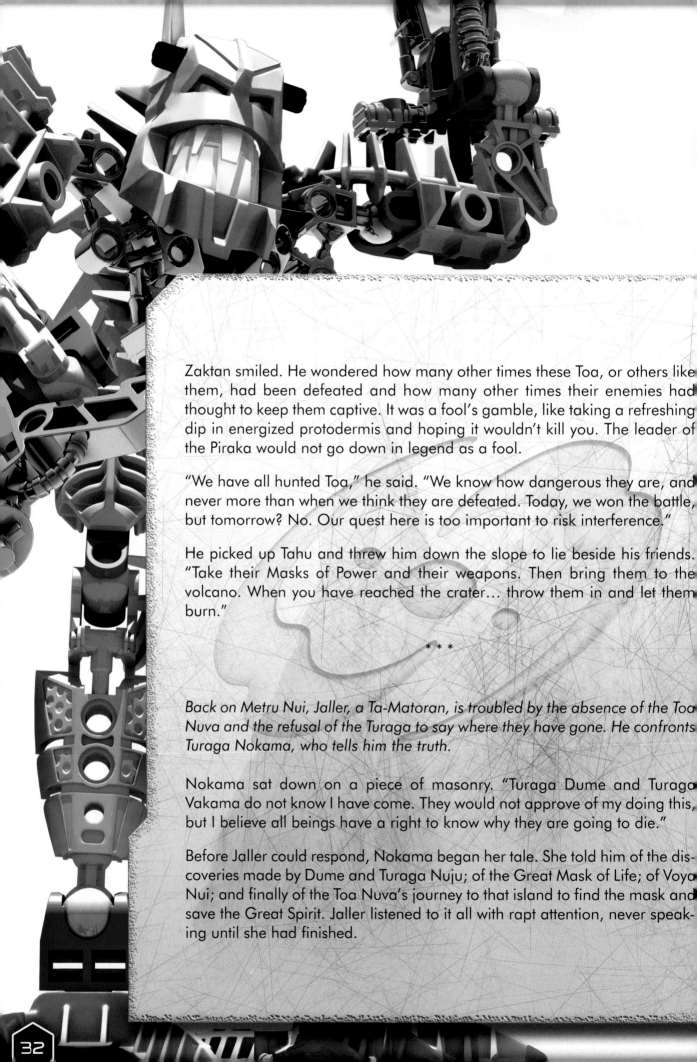

Zaktan smiled. He wondered how many other times these Toa, or others like them, had been defeated and how many other times their enemies had thought to keep them captive. It was a fool's gamble, like taking a refreshing dip in energized protodermis and hoping it wouldn't kill you. The leader of the Piraka would not go down in legend as a fool.

"We have all hunted Toa," he said. "We know how dangerous they are, and never more than when we think they are defeated. Today, we won the battle, but tomorrow? No. Our quest here is too important to risk interference."

He picked up Tahu and threw him down the slope to lie beside his friends. "Take their Masks of Power and their weapons. Then bring them to the volcano. When you have reached the crater... throw them in and let them burn."

* * *

Back on Metru Nui, Jaller, a Ta-Matoran, is troubled by the absence of the Toa Nuva and the refusal of the Turaga to say where they have gone. He confronts Turaga Nokama, who tells him the truth.

Nokama sat down on a piece of masonry. "Turaga Dume and Turaga Vakama do not know I have come. They would not approve of my doing this, but I believe all beings have a right to know why they are going to die."

Before Jaller could respond, Nokama began her tale. She told him of the discoveries made by Dume and Turaga Nuju; of the Great Mask of Life; of Voya Nui; and finally of the Toa Nuva's journey to that island to find the mask and save the Great Spirit. Jaller listened to it all with rapt attention, never speaking until she had finished.

"If Mata Nui dies…" he began.

"Then must not the universe die with him?" said Nokama. "Up to now, the Toa have fought to bring light and hope back to the Matoran. If they had failed, and Makuta triumphed, at least we would have been alive to nurture a dream of a better future. If they fail this time… there will be no future."

"And there has been no word of them?" asked Jaller.

"None. Dume believes that if they were going to return, they would be back by now … I am sorry to have burdened you with this, Jaller, for there is nothing that can be done. But at least now, when the stars are extinguished and the end comes, you will understand."

Without another word, Turaga Nokama departed, leaving Jaller to ponder her message. The news was devastating but it did not leave him feeling lost or hopeless.

There is something I can do, he decided. *But I will not tell Takanuva or the Turaga – they would only try to stop me, and every moment matters now.*

He ran from the ruins, plans already forming in his brain. He would need help – the best, most trustworthy, and bravest Matoran he could find – and then they would go to Voya Nui themselves. They would find the Toa Nuva and this Mask of Life, they would help to save the Great Spirit. Somehow, they would make things right.

You don't have to be a Toa to be a hero, he thought. *You just have to be willing to fight for what matters most.*

* * *

ZAKTAN "THE SNAKE"

Leader of the Piraka who invaded the island of Voya Nui in search [of] the Mask of Life. Zaktan was working as a slave in a protoder[m] mine when he was recruited into the Dark Hunters. After leading [an] unsuccessful rebellion against The Shadowed One, that bein[g's] devastating eyebeams somehow turned Zaktan's body from so[lid] matter to mass of microscopic protodites. He now had the abilit[y to] disperse his body into a swarm of the tiny creatures, slipping throu[gh] any opening, no matter how small, and flying on the wind.

Zaktan defected from the Dark Hunters with five others and form[ed] the Piraka. Under the influence of Makuta Teridax, they invaded a[nd] conquered Voya Nui and enslaved the Matoran population. Zakta[n's] team defeated the Toa Nuva and allied with Brutaka, but we[re] unable to stop the Toa Inika from claiming the mask. Mutated by [the] waters around Voya Nui into snake-like creatures, they we[re] captured by Axonn and imprisoned on the island of Daxia.

Zaktan possessed elemental air power, which could only be used [in] combination with another Piraka. He also had laser vision, a[nd] carried a three-bladed sword made out of protodites and a zam[or] sphere launcher.

100% CUNNING
0% CUDDLY

THOK "DRIFTER"

One of the six Piraka who invaded Voya Nui, Thok was an expert at manipulating others and then abandoning them when things went wrong. From the beginning, Thok knew and counted on the fact that none of the Piraka trusted each other. He made alliances with each of the other five, promising to share the power of the Mask of Life with them, when he had no intention to do so.

Along with Hakann, Thok stole the power of Brutaka and tried to wipe out the Toa Inika and the other Piraka. However, Hakann and Thok turned on each other and gave the Toa the chance to strike back. Using a zamor sphere created by Zaktan, Toa Hewkii struck both combatants at once, draining the power they had stolen back into Brutaka. He is currently imprisoned on Daxia.

Thok carried an ice peg gun and a zamor sphere launcher, possessed spellbinder vision that could disorient opponents, and had the power to bring inanimate objects to life under his control. He also had elemental ice power that could only be used in combination with the powers of another Piraka.

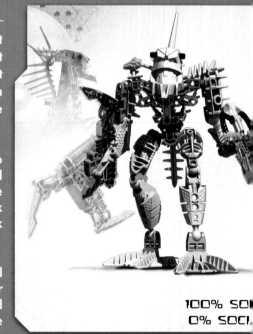

100% SO[
0% SOCI[

REIDAK "TRACER"

The strongest of the six Piraka, Reidak was also quite intellige[nt] though he rarely showed that. During the initial fight with the T[oa] Nuva on Voya Nui, Reidak was able to break one of Lewa's [two] katana and it took the power of three Toa to temporarily defeat hi[m]. What the Toa did not realize was that Reidak had the ability to ada[pt] to any defeat, so he could not be beaten the same way twice.

Reidak was a highly skilled hunter and loved destruction. Though [he] was intelligent enough to make plans, he didn't bother. He felt [he] was strong enough to beat any opponent without having to come [up] with a strategy first. He disliked Avak a great deal, since the pris[ons] created by Avak were the one trap he could not escape. He is n[ow] imprisoned on Daxia.

Reidak carried a zamor sphere launcher and a combinati[on] buzzsaw-drill tool. He possessed infrared and thermal imagi[ng] vision and elemental earth power, which could only be used [in]

100% HUNTER
0% CHICKEN

AVAK "TRIGGER"

100% ARMS
0% CHARMS

The engineer and jailer of the Piraka team, Avak was responsible for the construction of the zamor sphere launchers used in the invasion of Voya Nui. Ambitious and sharp, he sensed from the start that something was not right with the team's pursuit of the Mask of Life, but never realized they were being influenced by Teridax.

Avak battled the Toa Nuva alongside the other Piraka, at one point imprisoning Kopaka Nuva. A poor hand-to-hand fighter, Avak only liked to go into battle with a tool or weapon in his hand. Fortunately for him, he had the skill to make a weapon out of almost anything. Mutated along with the rest of the team, he is currently imprisoned on Daxia.

Avak carried a zamor sphere launcher and a seismic pick axe/jackhammer combination. He had the ability to mentally bring into being a perfect prison for any opponent which could counter any powers they might try to use to escape. He also possessed elemental stone power which could only be used in combination with another Piraka, and X-ray and telescopic vision.

VEZOK "BEAST"

The nastiest of the Piraka, Vezok was a key part of the strangest events in that team's history. While looting Makuta Teridax's lair at Mangaia, they came upon the Spear of Fusion. Toying with it, Hakann accidentally unleashed a burst of energy which struck Vezok. The result was to split Vezok into two beings, the second being nicknamed Vezon (the Matoran world for "double"). Being only half an individual, Vezon was hopelessly mad, and Vezok was determined to one day be whole again.

Usually cool on the outside, Vezok was convinced the other Piraka were out to get him (which was correct) and particularly dislikes Hakann because of the Vezon incident. At one point, he made a deal with Reidak that they would share the power of the Mask of Life if they found it, abandoning the other four Piraka. Secretly, he intended to kill Reidak in that case and keep the mask for himself. He is currently imprisoned on Daxia.

Vezok carried a zamor sphere launcher and a combination harpoon/buzzsaw. He had impact vision and the ability to absorb the powers of others, store them, and use them himself later on. He also controlled the elemental power of water, though he could only use it in combination with other Piraka.

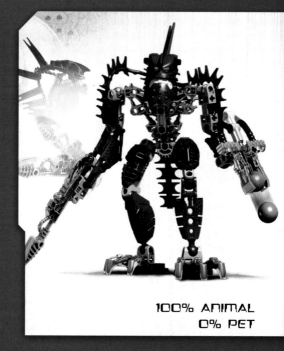

100% ANIMAL
0% PET

HAKANN

The most dangerous and cunning of the Piraka, there was no one Hakann would not betray. He clashed repeatedly with Zaktan and the others, sabotaged Vezok's canister in a failed attempt to kill him, and even informed the Dark Hunters where the Piraka were and what they were after. He was almost casually cruel, once explaining that he had vaporized a herd of Kikanalo because they were "blocking his view."

When Thok and Hakann successfully stole Brutaka's power, it seemed that they were certain to be able to claim the Mask of Life for themselves. But Hakann betrayed Thok, attacking him from behind, and the Toa Inika were able to take advantage of their fight to drain the excess power out of them. Hakann is currently a prisoner on Daxia.

Hakann carried a zamor sphere launcher and a lava launcher. He possessed heat vision, the ability to launch mental attacks, and the elemental power of fire (which could only be used in combination with other Piraka.)

100% EXPLOSIVE
0% FUSE

VOYA NUI

Voya Nui is the hiding place of the powerful Mask of Life. Once located in the center of a huge continent within the Matoran domes, it was torn free by a massive earthquake and sent rocketing up through its dome and into the open ocean above. It floated for hundreds of years before coming to rest where it was with a small population of surviving Matoran, Axonn and Brutaka. Voya Nui was the site of the battles between the Piraka and both the Toa Nuva and Toa Inika. It has since been returned to the land mass it came from.

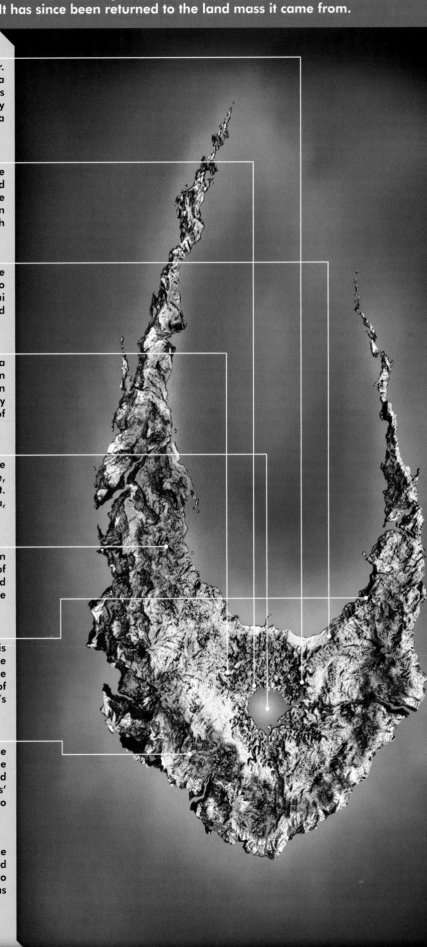

THE PIRAKA STRONGHOLD

A mighty fortress built by forced Matoran labor. This was the headquarters of the Piraka on Voya Nui and housed the crystal vat in which Makuta's energy form lurked. The stronghold was badly damaged by battles with the Toa Nuva and Toa Inika.

CHAMBER OF LIFE

A secret chamber beneath Mount Valmai, where the Mask of Life was kept hidden. It was guarded by Axonn, Brutaka, and Umbra. It could be reached by going through a hidden entrance in the Green Belt and descending a staircase with 777 stairs.

NUI CAVES

A network of caverns located beneath the surface of Voya Nui. Axonn led the Matoran down here to keep them safe from harm before Voya Nui returned to its native continent. Nektann could also be found down here.

DESERT OF SORROWS

A vast, arid expanse near the center of Voya Nui. The Toa Nuva briefly fought the Matoran Resistance here, due to a case of mistaken identity. Gali Nuva was cured of temporary insanity while in the desert thanks to the help of Axonn.

MOUNT VALMAI

An extremely active volcano, Mount Valmai is the highest peak on Voya Nui. The Chamber of Life, hiding place of the Mask of Life, rests beneath it. The Piraka once tried to empty the volcano of lava, believing the mask could be found that way.

THE GREEN BELT

This strange forest encircled the island, its origin unknown. Some of the Piraka believed the Mask of Life could be found here, and that its power had made the plants grow. The secret entrance to the Chamber of Life could be found here.

MATORAN CLIFF VILLAGE

Dwelling place of the Voya Nui Matoran, this village was heavily defended and constructed like a fortress. It was originally intended to protect the residents from dangerous Rahi. It was the site of the Piraka's ambush of most of the island's population and was later destroyed.

ZONE OF NIGHTMARES

A cavern found along the staircase leading to the Chamber of Life. Anyone entering it would see their worst fear brought to life. The Piraka faced Irnakk, a legendary monster of their species' mythology, and the Toa Inika were tricked into thinking they had killed the Toa Nuva here.

PIRAKA OUTPOSTS

Small guard stations located throughout the island, armed with robotic defense devices called Nektann. They were heavily armored and able to reconstruct themselves. One outpost was destroyed by Toa Nuparu using his laser drill.

e Matoran residents of Voya Nui iginally came from other lands. When eir Turaga felt they were not working rd enough, they were shipped to the alm of Karzahni, where they would be epaired." Unfortunately, Karzahni did poor job, resulting in the Matoran ing smaller and weaker than normal es. Angry over his failure, Karzahni ve the Matoran weapons and shipped em to the southern continent. They entually settled in Voya Nui.

hen Voya Nui was ripped from its ntinent and ended up in the outer ean, the Matoran found they had to uggle to survive in a hostile climate d with limited resources. But survive ey did, constructing new villages, tting up their own government, and orking together. (At the time, none of em realized the true significance of ya Nui – that it was the hiding place of e Mask of Life – or that Axonn and utaka shared the island with them.)

one of the Voya Nui Matoran had ever en a Toa face to face. So when the evil aka came to the island claiming to be a, most Matoran believed that was at they were. Only a handful estioned why "Toa" would be so nasty, structive and brutal.

hen the Piraka enslaved the Matoran pulation with zamor spheres, only six caped: Garan, Piruk, Velika, Kazi, Balta d Dalu. They formed the Matoran sistance, hiding in the mountains and rassing the Piraka. Although far weaker an their enemies, they did have some ccesses. These included the theft of a mor sphere launcher from Avak and at Piraka's subsequent defeat by Dalu.

sily their most important moment me during a major battle between the a Inika and the Piraka. The Matoran pped away from the fight and found here the Toa Nuva were being kept isoner. They succeeded in freeing the roes. Later, Velika would make a new katana for Lewa to replace the one e Piraka had broken.

ith their fellow Matoran freed from the aka's domination, the Matoran sistance remained on Voya Nui when e Toa Inika left to pursue the Mask of e. They are still there now, although e island itself has now rejoined its iginal continent.

GARAN Onu-Matoran leader of the Resistance on Voya Nui. Garan was a strategic thinker, who was convinced the Resistance could win as long as they worked together. He carried twin pulse bolt generators that fired a ball of energy which grew more powerful the further it traveled. Garan led the mission to invade the Piraka stronghold and rescue the imprisoned Toa Nuva.

PIRUK The Le-Matoran member of the Resistance, Piruk was known for his stealth. Not terribly brave, he was still extremely loyal to his friends and a very skilled spy. He carried two shredder claws which could rip through solid metal. Piruk learned much of the Piraka's plans by sneaking into the Piraka stronghold and eavesdropping on Zaktan.

BALTA Ta-Matoran member of the Resistance, Balta was the weapons maker for the team and one of the most daring of the group. He stole a zamor sphere launcher from Avak, enabling Velika to copy the design, and also led the rescue party for Garan when he was a prisoner of the Piraka. Balta carried twin repeller tools which could block an enemy and strike back with equal force.

DALU Ga-Matoran warrior of the Resistance, Dalu was the best fighter on the team. Her most important moment during the battle against the Piraka was her single-handed defeat of Avak. Her twin chargers allowed her to temporarily increase one attribute of a target (strength, speed, hearing, etc.)

KAZI Ko-Matoran member of the Resistance, Kazi was cool, quiet and secretive. He was the first Voya Nui Matoran to meet Axonn and the only one who had an idea that there might be more to Voya Nui than anyone knew. He carried twin echo forks which, when slammed together, produced a devastating sound wave.

VELIKA Eccentric Po-Matoran Resistance member, Velika was known for his habit of always speaking in riddles and metaphors. A skilled engineer, he created the zamor sphere launchers carried by the Toa Inika as well as the energized protodermis-filled zamor spheres they used. Velika carried twin power carvers.

Brutaka

Axonn

AXONN AND BRUTAKA

Axonn and Brutaka were members of the Order of Mata Nui and long-time friends. Axonn started out as member of the Order's predecessor, the Hand of Artakha, and served with that organization until it broke u He then put his warrior skills to work conquering a number of southern lands before being recruited into t Order. Brutaka's early years were spent as a lieutenant in the Brotherhood of Makuta's forces before the Ord sought him out. He worked for many years as a roving agent, dealing with whatever trouble might come up the universe.

The Order eventually reassigned them both to Voya Nui, where they would have the important job guarding the Mask of Life. They would spend most of the next 100,000 years there. Both did their jobs well, b over the last 1000 years or so, Brutaka became restless. He began to feel that perhaps the Great Spirit Mo Nui had abandoned this universe or simply no longer cared. And he started to think that perhaps he should ta the Mask of Life for himself.

When the Piraka invaded Voya Nui, Brutaka violated every law of the Order by allying himself with them. H helped them defeat the Toa Nuva and joined them in battling the Toa Inika. His ultimate plan was to have t Piraka get the mask, then steal it away from them. But he ran into a setback when Hakann and Thok struck him and stole his power.

Brutaka eventually got his energies back, thanks to the heroic actions of the Toa Inika. But he was st determined to seize the mask. In the heart of the Piraka stronghold, he fought Axonn. Although Brutaka de out enormous punishment to his old friend, Axonn kept coming, finally defeating Brutaka with a powerful blo Brutaka was then transported to the Pit, the maximum security prison run by the Order which housed only t worst criminals.

Axonn later acted to help the Toa retrieve the Mask of Life and single-handedly defeated the mutated Pirak He protected the Matoran on Voya Nui's journey back to its original homeland, and later left there to join in t Order's assault on the Brotherhood.

Brutaka escaped the Pit and reformed, even stealing the precious Staff of Artakha from Makuta Teridax. He w welcomed back into the Order and led a team of condemned villains on a mission to find and free the form leader of the Brotherhood of Makuta, Miserix. He has since been reunited with Axonn for the raid on t Brotherhood base at Destral.

Both Axonn and Brutaka had enormous power. Axonn wore the Kanohi Rode, the Mask of Truth, a carried an axe. Brutaka wore the Kanohi Olmak, the Mask of Dimensional Gates, and carri a twin-bladed sword.

TOA INIKA MATORO

Matoro was never comfortable with the idea of being a Toa. He was not a warrior like Jaller or Kongu, an athlete like Hewkii, a scholar like Hahli, or an inventor like Nuparu. He was simply a translator for Turaga Nuju, and certainly not qualified to be a hero as far as he was concerned.

Still, he did his best, battling the Piraka with great courage. When the Toa Inika entered the Chamber of Death on the journey to find the Mask of Life, Matoro volunteered to die so the others could go on. He perished, but was immediately brought back to life – for the chamber's test was all about the willingness to die for a cause, not the actual end of existence. Later, Toa Kongu discovered that Matoro was the destined wearer of the Mask of Life, but he kept this secret even from Matoro for some time.

Following the defeat of the Piraka, Makuta Teridax briefly possessed Matoro's body during a time when the Toa's spirit was absent. He attempted to corrupt the Toa, but they discovered the truth and forced him to leave Matoro's body by threatening to destroy it. Matoro's spirit then returned to his own body.

As the Toa Inika of Ice, Matoro wore the Kanohi Iden, the Mask of Spirit, and carried an energized ice sword and a zamor sphere launcher.

TOA INIKA JALLER

Jaller led his team of Matoran on a dangerous expedition from Metru Nui to Voya Nui in search of the missing Toa Nuva. They arrived via Toa canisters, but as they were about to emerge, lightning bolts from a red star high above struck the canisters. The six Matoran were transformed into the super-charged Toa Inika.

As team leader, Jaller set out to learn from the mistakes of Vakama and Tahu. Rather than just give orders and charge ahead, he tried to take the time to listen to and learn from his teammates. Although he was always brave in battle, he could not escape the memory of dying as a Matoran on the island of Mata Nui. Even though he was returned to life by Takutanuva, the experience sometimes made him hesitate at crucial moments.

Jaller led the fight with the Piraka and Brutaka. He almost volunteered to sacrifice his life for the mission in the Chamber of Death, but Matoro spoke up first. Jaller was also responsible for stopping Vezon and Kardas, using a special zamor sphere given to him by Axonn.

As the Toa Inika of Fire, Jaller wore the Kanohi Calix, the Mask of Fate, and carried an energized flame sword and a zamor sphere launcher.

TOA INIKA HAHLI

Although Hahli accepted her transformation into a Toa as a part of her destiny, she was never completely comfortable with the power she now controlled. When the Toa Inika were briefly tricked into believing they had slain the Toa Nuva, Hahli openly questioned whether Toa simply had too much power for any one being to handle. She advised Jaller that the team should turn back. He talked her into continuing by reminding her that they owed it to the memory of all the Toa who had died fighting for justice to keep going.

Hahli joined with Jaller and two members of the Matoran Resistance, Dalu and Piruk, on a successful mission to save enslaved villagers. Along the way, she argued with Dalu, who felt that Hahli had too optimistic a view of life.

When the Mask of Life plunged into the ocean, Hahli dove to pursue it. She went down as deep as she could before being overwhelmed by the sudden change in pressure and blacking out. She was saved by a Matoran of Mahri Nui, who died himself in the effort to rescue her.

As the Toa Inika of Water, Hahli wore the Kanohi Elda, or Mask of Detection, which could find the Mask of Life wherever it might be hidden. She also carried a laser harpoon and a zamor sphere launcher.

TOA INIKA HEWKII

When Hewkii became a Toa, he had one thought in mind: the faster the Toa Inika found the Mask of Life, the faster he could get back to Metru Nui, to his friends and to his old life. He didn't want to waste time on complicated strategies or long-range plans. Instead, he preferred the "smash everything until you find what you want" approach.

Hewkii joined with Matoro and two members of the Matoran Resistance, Kazi and Balta, to free captured Matoran. But the two villagers instead took the heroes to a remote region of the island. There they came upon a wounded Axonn, who had lost a battle with Brutaka. Warned by him that Brutaka was after the Mask of Life, Hewkii and Matoro rushed to the Piraka stronghold to aid their friends in battle.

When Hakann and Thok stole the powers of Brutaka and transformed into even more dangerous menaces, it was Hewkii's accurate shot with a zamor sphere launcher that ended their threat. Jaller later named Hewkii as deputy leader of the team. When Makuta Teridax possessed Matoro's body, Hewkii was the first to notice something was seriously wrong.

As the Toa Inika of Stone, Hewkii wore the Kanohi Sanok, the Mask of Accuracy, and carried a laser axe, climbing chain, and zamor sphere launcher.

TOA INIKA KONGU

Becoming a Toa posed some unique challenges for Kongu. First, he was unhappy that Toa Nuparu got the Mask of Flight instead of him – he, after all, was the master of Air. Then he discovered the mask he did have, which gave him telepathic powers, couldn't be turned off. He spent the entire adventure on Voya Nui having to hear the thoughts of everyone around him.

Kongu teamed with Nuparu and two Matoran resistance members, Garan and Velika. Together, they destroyed a Nektann and managed to find the Toa Nuva's masks. Ambushed by the Piraka, Kongu was able to defeat Avak by increasing the air pressure around the Piraka until he dropped.

When the Inika were tricked into believing they had killed the Toa Nuva, it was Kongu who exposed the hoax when he told his friends that he had sensed no thoughts from the "Nuva" – meaning they had to be illusions. Later, he used the Mask of Telepathy to read the mind of the Mask of Life and discovered that Matoro was the destined wearer of that powerful Kanohi.

As a Toa Inika of Air, Kongu wore the Kanohi Suletu, the Mask of Telepathy. He carried a zamor sphere launcher and a laser crossbow.

TOA INIKA NUPARU

As a Matoran and as a Toa, one thing stayed the same for Nuparu: he loved to learn. To him, being a Toa meant more chances to see places and do things he would never have had the chance to do in his former life. At times, he became so fascinated by some new Rahi or new location that he would forget what he was supposed to be doing.

Nuparu showed himself to be a brave and resourceful Toa, defeating both a Nektann and the powerful Zaktan on his own. With some help from Kongu, he finally mastered the power of the Mask of Flight. This made him an excellent scout for the team.

Nuparu formed a friendship with Velika during his time on Voya Nui, as both were skilled inventors. Despite some early tension, even Kongu eventually came to respect the Toa of Earth. Nuparu showed that success as a Toa had less to do with what power you possessed, but being quick-witted enough to know how to use it. A good example of this was his battle with Zaktan, in which he scattered the enemy's protodites by flying directly into the swarm and then rotating rapidly to sweep them into his wake.

As a Toa Inika of Earth, Nuparu wore the Kanohi Kadin, the Mask of Flight. He carried a zamor sphere launcher and a laser drill.

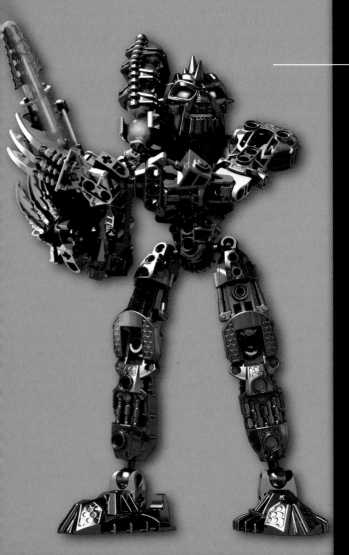

UMBRA

A guardian of the Mask of Life, Umbra lived deep beneath the surface of Voya Nui. He was the first guardian put in place by the Great Beings for the mask, more than 100,000 years ago. Umbra was capable of turning into pure light and wore skates that allowed him to move at super-speed. He was armed with a staff that fired lasers and a Rhotuka spinner that could create hard light projections. Umbra challenged the Toa Inika in battle and was defeated in battle when Toa Inika Matoro used his ice power to create glassy surfaces that Umbra's light form bounced off of until he was unconscious.

Umbra remains on Voya Nui, waiting for the return of the Mask of Life to its resting place.

VEZON

Vezon traveled to Voya Nui in search of the Mask of Life, only to find himself fused to it and forced to remain as its guardian. He was partnered with a monstrous spider, Fenrakk, and given two powers by the mask: the ability to see a limited time forward into the future, and the ability to absorb the kinetic energy of any blow directed against him. He was also granted immortality for as long as he wore the mask.

The Piraka challenged Vezon and were easily defeated, but the Toa Inika managed to beat him and take the mask. With the mask gone, all of Vezon's powers left too. He was later captured by the Order of Mata Nui and sent with others on a mission to find the long-missing Makuta Miserix.

RACE FOR THE MASK OF LIFE

Both the Toa Inika and the Piraka wanted the Mask of Life, but for different reasons – the Inika to save the life of Mata Nui, the Piraka for their own personal power. The race was on to seize the legendary artifact of power.

The Piraka got a head start, discovering the secret entrance in the Green Belt that led to the underground hiding place of the mask. They first found themselves in a zone of nightmares, where their greatest fears would become real. Here they faced Irnakk, a mythological creature among their species. Irnakk had the power to convert an opponent into pure thought and then draw him into its twisted mind. It easily defeated five of the six Piraka, but Zaktan refused to surrender. Claiming that he had already been through far worse than Irnakk could ever do to him, Zaktan threatened to bring down the ceiling of the chamber and kill himself and the other Piraka. With no one alive to fear him, Irnakk would cease to exist. Knowing this, Irnakk backed down.

Moving on, the Piraka found themselves trapped in six stone cages. A voice told them that they could escape, but only if they all opened their cages at the exact same time. If any one of them opened his cage early, he would survive, and the rest would perish. Reidak betrayed the group, with the result that all six fell into deep water. Though they eventually escaped, exposure to the water had already begun to mutate them.

Meanwhile, the Toa had encountered their own set of challenges. In the zone of nightmares, they fought beings they believed were their greatest enemies, accidentally killing them. The dead foes were then revealed to be the Toa Nuva in disguise. This led the Toa to doubt whether they could control their own powers. But these Toa Nuva were later exposed to be just illusions, as was the Toa Lhikan figure who warned them not to go on.

The Toa Inika then journeyed to the Chamber of Death. Here they were told that one of their number had to die for the rest to be allowed to go on. Although Jaller wanted to volunteer to make the sacrifice, Matoro spoke up first. The Toa of Ice was destroyed and then recreated and the Inika were allowed to pass on.

heir next challenge was perhaps their greatest on
e journey. They were confronted by Umbra, a
owerful guardian of the Mask of Life, and the
rotodax. These creatures were giant-sized versions
f the microscopic protodites, but with a special
ower: every time one was struck, it would split into
vo of the creatures, making their numbers grow
apidly in battle. The protodax were driven off by
mbra's approach, but the Inika still had to
vercome the guardian and his light-based powers.
the end, Toa Matoro and Toa Nuparu teamed up
defeat Umbra.

eyond that chamber, the Toa Inika came to a vast
lain bisected by a river of lava. At the end of a
ridge, they saw a gateway to the Chamber of Life
here the mask was hidden. The Piraka ambushed
e Toa there, and though the bridge itself was
estroyed by Toa Kongu, the Piraka won the fight.

ntering the Chamber of Life, the Piraka found
emselves faced with Vezon and Fenrakk. Vezok,
ho had hated Vezon since being into two beings,
w this as his chance for revenge, But Vezon used
is Spear of Fusion to merge Vezok and Reidak into
monstrous new being. This creature defeated the
st of the Piraka and then was separated back into
vo Piraka by Vezon. The experience so drained
ezok and Reidak that they could not fight back.

t this point, the Toa Inika appeared. They did
attle with Vezon and Fenrakk, overcoming them,
nd then faced the might of Vezon and Kardas (the
ansformed version of Fenrakk). Beating the evil
air, the Toa claimed the Mask of Life.

ut the Piraka were not yet done. They confronted
e Toa one last time, only to be temporarily halted
their tracks by Hewkii's power. A sudden attack
y Kardas caused Matoro to lose the mask, which
ew off on its own out of the chamber and up the
reat staircase, with the Toa Inika in pursuit.

reaking free after the Toa departed, they were
eady to go after them when Vezok halted the
roup. He wanted them to use the Spear of Fusion
merge himself and Vezon into one being again.
ngered by Vezok's refusal to go on until this was
one, Reidak snapped the spear into multiple
ieces. The Piraka went after the Toa then, leaving
ezon and Kardas behind.

FENRAKK

The Fenrakk spider was the partner/pet of Vezon. Like its
master, it too could absorb the kinetic energy of blows directed
against it and grow stronger. Fenrakk could not truly be
beaten as long as Vezon wore the mask – if defeated it would
simply transform into another kind of creature.

Fenrakk possessed enormous strength and acidic saliva. It
was defeated by the Toa Inika and transformed into the
Kardas Dragon. Smaller versions of the Fenrakk spider were
seen on Voya Nui, making it likely that this specimen was
mutated by the Mask of Life.

KARDAS

When Vezon and Fenrakk were defeated by the Toa Inika and
fell into a lava river, both emerged unharmed — but Fenrakk
had mutated into the monstrous Kardas dragon. Huge and
winged, Kardas constantly generated energy and could
release it through blasts from its mouth. It was defeated by
the Toa Inika and later abandoned by Vezon.

Escaping the Chamber of Life, Kardas traveled to the surface
of Voya Nui, where it battled the giant Rahi Tahtorak.
Following that fight, it flew to Mata Nui, where it lost a battle
with the reawakened Bohrok. After being cared for and
partially healed by Gali Nuva, it traveled to Metru Nui and
has since been captured and placed in the Archives.

* * *

The Mask Lost

The Toa Inika have found the Mask of Life at last… but can they keep it?

The effect of the zamor sphere on Vezon and Kardas had faded. Although it left both too weak to be a threat for the moment, Kardas was not going to be defeated so easily. As the beast collapsed, it unleashed one last blast of energy that struck Matoro. The shock made him lose his grip on the Mask of Life.

The Piraka started forward, ready to scramble for the mask when it hit the ground – except it never did fall to the floor. Instead, it hovered in mid-air before flashing out of the chamber almost too fast for the eye to follow. It was headed back the way the Toa and Piraka had come. Zaktan and his team turned to go after it. The Toa Inika ran forward too, determined to get it first.

"Hewkii!" Jaller shouted, pointing at the Piraka.

The Toa Inika of Stone nodded and loosed his elemental powers on the enemy. Stone vises erupted from the floor to grab all six Piraka and hold them fast. Zaktan avoided the trap by dissipating into a swarm of protodites, only to be flash frozen in the next moment by Matoro.

"That buys us maybe ten seconds," said Hewkii.

"Then that will have to be enough," Jaller replied, racing up the staircase.

The six Toa Inika ran as if their very universe depended on it, for in truth it did. So fast were they moving that they did not notice the words of fire forming on the stairs beneath their feet… the words that read:

> *Beware the depths of darkness*
> *That wait with chill embrace,*
> *For those doomed to dwell within the pit*
> *Can never leave that place.*
> *No one will know your fate*
> *If taken by the shadowed sea,*
> *Only whispers of the waves will say*
> *Death has at last claimed thee.*

The Toa Inika were lucky. Their passage back up the staircase had been unimpeded by guardians. Apparently, the mask's protectors were in place to stop anyone from reaching the lower chamber, not those fleeing from it.

Still, the mask managed to stay just ahead of them. Attempts to use elemental

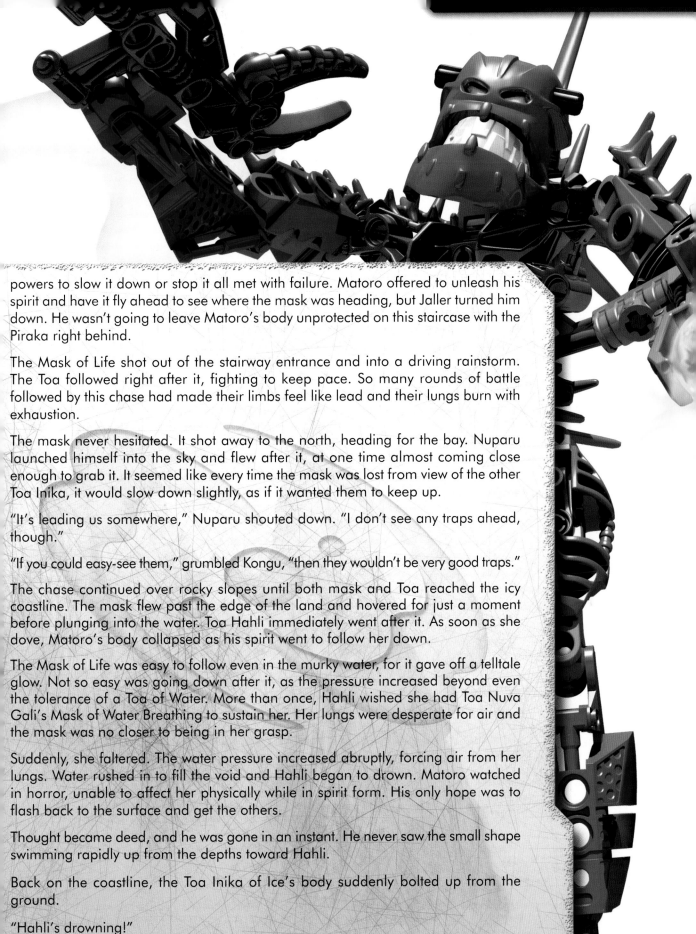

powers to slow it down or stop it all met with failure. Matoro offered to unleash his spirit and have it fly ahead to see where the mask was heading, but Jaller turned him down. He wasn't going to leave Matoro's body unprotected on this staircase with the Piraka right behind.

The Mask of Life shot out of the stairway entrance and into a driving rainstorm. The Toa followed right after it, fighting to keep pace. So many rounds of battle followed by this chase had made their limbs feel like lead and their lungs burn with exhaustion.

The mask never hesitated. It shot away to the north, heading for the bay. Nuparu launched himself into the sky and flew after it, at one time almost coming close enough to grab it. It seemed like every time the mask was lost from view of the other Toa Inika, it would slow down slightly, as if it wanted them to keep up.

"It's leading us somewhere," Nuparu shouted down. "I don't see any traps ahead, though."

"If you could easy-see them," grumbled Kongu, "then they wouldn't be very good traps."

The chase continued over rocky slopes until both mask and Toa reached the icy coastline. The mask flew past the edge of the land and hovered for just a moment before plunging into the water. Toa Hahli immediately went after it. As soon as she dove, Matoro's body collapsed as his spirit went to follow her down.

The Mask of Life was easy to follow even in the murky water, for it gave off a telltale glow. Not so easy was going down after it, as the pressure increased beyond even the tolerance of a Toa of Water. More than once, Hahli wished she had Toa Nuva Gali's Mask of Water Breathing to sustain her. Her lungs were desperate for air and the mask was no closer to being in her grasp.

Suddenly, she faltered. The water pressure increased abruptly, forcing air from her lungs. Water rushed in to fill the void and Hahli began to drown. Matoro watched in horror, unable to affect her physically while in spirit form. His only hope was to flash back to the surface and get the others.

Thought became deed, and he was gone in an instant. He never saw the small shape swimming rapidly up from the depths toward Hahli.

Back on the coastline, the Toa Inika of Ice's body suddenly bolted up from the ground.

"Hahli's drowning!"

The other Toa made for the water, Jaller already figuring out a rescue plan. He never had to use it. Hahli's body suddenly appeared on the surface. All five Inika wondered if they had been too late, and their companion was dead.

Then she sputtered and coughed, the sweetest sound any of the Inika had ever heard. Jaller went to pull her back to shore. That was when he noticed someone was already holding her.

A head broke the surface, wearing a Kanohi mask. It was a Matoran! Toa Jaller helped both him and Hahli to the beach. The Toa of Water was already recovering, but the Matoran collapsed as soon as he hit land.

"Who are you?" said Jaller. "Where did you come from?"

"No time," gasped the Matoran. "Help us… city beneath the sea… help us or we're lost…"

"What city?" asked Hewkii. "What are you talking about?"

But the Matoran wasn't saying any more. His heartlight stopped shining and his eyes faded to black. He was dead.

Matoro stood over the body of the unfortunate villager.

"Mata Nui watch over him."

"He sacrificed his life to save mine," said Toa Hahli. "That may make him a greater hero than any of us."

"And he brought us more mysteries," said Hewkii. "Who was this Matoran? What killed him? What city was he talking about? And why did the Mask of Life vanish beneath the waves?"

"Maybe fate random-picked the wrong Matoran to be Toa," said Kongu. "We failed."

"No, Toa-hero, you succeeded," a familiar voice said. "Now you just have to succeed again."

Kongu and the other Toa Inika whirled in surprise. Coming down the beach, led by Axonn and the six members of the Matoran resistance, were the Toa Nuva. All of them had their Kanohi Nuva masks and their equipment and looked none the worse for their experiences on the island.

"Tahu!" Jaller shouted. "Gali! I can't believe it!"

"We were afraid you might be dead!" said Hahli. "It's so wonderful to see you. Now everything will be all right."

"Toa are hard to kill, you know that," said Pohatu Nuva, smiling. "Ask Makuta… if he ever gets out from under that door."

"Our Matoran friends found us," said Tahu Nuva, "and freed us from the effects of the Piraka's zamor spheres. One even offered to forge a new air katana for Lewa. By the way, where are the Piraka?"

Jaller swiftly related the events leading up to the discovery and loss of the Mask of Life. Tahu listened intently, and reacted with surprise to the news that a Matoran civilization might lie hidden under the sea.

"We were trying to come up with a way to follow the mask when you arrived," said Jaller. "But now that you're here, you can go with us."

"Or maybe you would rather we just went back to Metru Nui?" asked Nuparu. Secretly, he hoped the Toa Nuva would brush aside that question. Having tasted the adventure of being a Toa, he had no wish to go back to guard duty on Metru Nui.

The six Toa Nuva glanced at each other. Kopaka nodded. Gali put a reassuring hand on Tahu's shoulder. Then the Toa Nuva of Fire turned back to the Toa Inika.

"I think, perhaps, it is we who should return to the city," Tahu said. "Take your team, Jaller, and find the mask."

"What?" Jaller said, stunned. "But you are Toa Nuva – the most powerful of all Toa – and this is your destiny!"

"It is our destiny to awaken Mata Nui from his centuries-long slumber," Kopaka corrected. "You are fighting to save the life of the Great Spirit, which must be done before he can be returned to consciousness. And that, my friends, is your destiny – not ours."

"We came to Voya Nui to find the Mask of Life," said Gali Nuva. "We failed. If it were not for you six, we and the Matoran of this island would still be enslaved to the Piraka … or worse. Don't you see? Your very existence as Toa is a sign from the Great Beings that you were meant to find the mask and save Mata Nui."

Jaller didn't want to accept it, but he knew there was truth in Gali's words. Where the Toa Nuva had met defeat, his team of Toa Inika had succeeded, at least temporarily. That had to mean something, unless the universe was just playing a cruel joke.

"What about the Matoran here?" asked Hahli. "The Piraka are still on the loose. The villagers are still in danger."

Tahu Nuva hesitated before replying. He hadn't thought of that. Back on Metru Nui, the Matoran had the Toa of Light and the Turaga to look after them while the Toa Nuva were away. Here there were no Turaga or Toa to serve as protectors. Should they take the Matoran back with them to Metru Nui?

Before a decision could be reached, Axonn spoke up.

"There is no need to be concerned," he said. "I will remain on Voya Nui and see to the Matoran. We will rebuild their lives here, until destiny says it is time for them to leave."

Jaller didn't know what to say. Axonn had been a mighty ally, and the Toa Nuva far more than that. How could he and his friends say goodbye? And with the mask out of reach under the ocean, was there even a point to a farewell?

As if anticipating his worries, Axonn spoke again.

"Fear not, my friend. There is way to reach the undersea realm, but the way is trea-cherous… and your destination a place of death and despair. But if you are willing to make the journey, my axe can open the way for you."

This time, Jaller did not look to his partners for their consent. He already knew what their answer would be.

"We'll do it," he said.

* * *

THE ZYGLAK

The Zyglak are a humanoid, reptilian race created by mistake when the Great Beings were making the first krana. Having no use for the Zyglak, the Great Beings rejected them. Although they were allowed to live in the Matoran universe, they had no role to play, no place to call home, and no reason for being. Over time, they grew bitter and hostile and became a danger to all who lived.

Zyglak took to hiding in ruins and other dark places where few ever ventured. It's said they were responsible for the death of all but one of the members of the first Toa team in history. Zyglak are immune to elemental attack, can spread a plague on contact, and carry spears and knives that can destroy any target on contact.

The Toa Inika encountered Zyglak in the cord leading to Mahri Nui and barely escaped with their lives. On their return journey to Voya Nui, they discovered all the Zyglak dead, murdered by the mutated Piraka. Zyglak later allied with Makuta Spiriah in a failed attempt to invade the island of Zakaz.

HYDRAXON

The original Hydraxon was a member of the Order of Mata Nui, the jailer of the Pit, and the trainer of the Toa Mata. He was killed when the prisoners of the Pit escaped. Later, when the Mask of Life needed a new warrior, it transformed a Matoran named Dekar into a duplicate of Hydraxon. This new Hydraxon had the memories of the old and no idea he had once been a Matoran. He clashed with the Toa Mahri, Nocturn, and the Maxilos robot.

Hydraxon was armed with a Cordak blaster, back blades, wrist blades, and explosive boomerangs. He remains in the ocean, hunting down escaped prisoners and jailing them again.

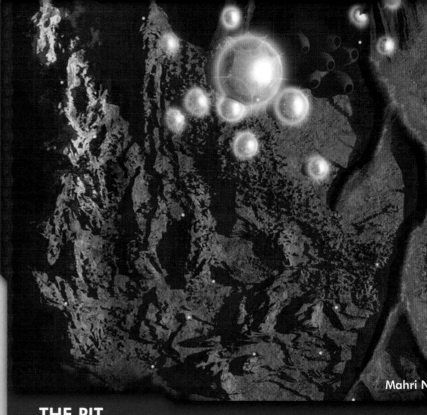

Mahri N

THE PIT

Ages ago, the Order of Mata Nui established a domed prison for t very worst criminals in the universe. Guarded by Hydraxon and t Maxilos series of robots, it was believed that no one could escape fro it. The Order named the place "the Pit," and over time, it held t Barraki warlords and others.

One thousand years ago, a terrible earthquake rocked the ent universe. It split open the roof of the Pit, allowing water from the oce outside to flood in, and damaged the prison cells. The inmat escaped, overwhelming and killing Hydraxon and making their w to the ocean above. What they did not realize was that the disas had resulted in the waters becoming charged with an energy that cou cause mutations in anyone exposed to it. Most of the escapees fou themselves transformed to water-breathers, and many suffer shocking physical changes. Now trapped in the ocean due to th inability to breathe air, the escaped prisoners called their new hor "the Pit" as well.

A millennium later, the Toa Inika traveled to the Pit in search of t Mask of Life. The mask was in danger at the time, having been seiz by the evil Barraki. It reached out with its power and transformed t Inika, changing their masks, armor and weapons and making the water-breathers. Now they were ready to fight for the fate of t universe in the depths of the Pit!

The first discovery the Toa made was a Matoran village under the se called "Mahri Nui" by its inhabitants. After first being suspicious of t heroes, the Matoran came to realize the Toa were there to defe them, and they named the team "Toa Mahri."

Rahi transpor

TOA MAHRI HAHLI

hen the Toa Inika became Toa Mahri, Hahli
ddenly became the team's strongest member.
e was in her element – water – and her skill at
imming and diving made her the best suited to
ttle the Barraki beneath the sea.

ahli was the one who managed to convince the
atoran of Mahri Nui that the Toa were there to
lp, not harm, them. When the Toa first
countered the Barraki, she tricked the villains
to believing she and her teammates were also
caped prisoners. When the Barraki imprisoned
e team, Hahli used her mask to copy the
pnotic power of a sea creature and so slip past
e squid that guarded her.

ter defeating the Barraki Mantax in battle, Hahli
oled him into believing the other Barraki were
out to betray him. Mantax formed an alliance
ith her and planned to attack his teammates.
t her plan backfired when the unexpected
terference of Hydraxon made it possible for
antax to steal the Mask of Life.

a Toa Mahri, Hahli wore the Kanohi Faxon, the
ask of Kindred, which allowed her to duplicate
e powers of sea creatures. She carried a
rdak blaster and protosteel talons.

TOA MAHRI MATORO

Matoro had spent many years keeping secrets
the result of having heard so many as Turago
Nuju's translator. But the secret he had to keep ir
the Pit was the hardest of all. Captured b
Hydraxon (who mistook him for an escapec
prisoner), Matoro was freed by the Maxilos sentry
robot – only to discover the robot was possessec
by the spirit of Makuta Teridax! Fearing his friends
might be killed if they attacked Teridax, or that the
Mask of Life might be lost in the struggle, he dic
not tell the other Toa what he had discovered.

Teridax forced Matoro to help him find the body o
Toa Tuyet, a corrupt Toa who had once possessec
a powerful artifact called a Nui stone. Teridax
wanted the stone, but did not get it, and Matoro
finally turned on him and attacked. Although he
could only slow Teridax down, it was long enough
for Jaller to give Matoro the Mask of Life. Jalle
also told him that Kongu had revealed the truth
Matoro was the destined wearer of the mask.

Desperate to save Mata Nui, Matoro raced of
with the mask with the Barraki in pursuit. He was
too late – Mata Nui had died. But Matoro refusec
to give up. Diving into the core of the universe
he donned the mask. Its power turned his body
to raw energy and then used that energy to
restore life to the Great Spirit. Matoro died a hero
perhaps the greatest hero ever known.

As a Toa Mahri, Matoro wore the Kanohi Tryna
the Mask of Reanimation, which could bring bacl
the dead to a semblance of life. He carried a
Cordak blaster and twin cutters.

TOA MAHRI JALLER

At first, Jaller found the Toa's experiences in the Pit to be extremely frustrating. Matoro, now knowing he was the destined wearer of the Mask of Life, was taking on more of a leadership role. Hahli, happy to be in her native element, kept swimming off on her own. Worst of all, as a Toa of Fire he had to struggle even to use his element in the depths of the sea. Still, Jaller knew the most important thing was the mission they must achieve. He fought bravely against the Barraki, led the evacuation of the Mahri Nui Matoran to Voya Nui, and succeeded in obtaining the Mask of Life and passing it on to Matoro.

When Mata Nui died, Matoro insisted the Toa continue to try and save him. Jaller told Matoro to go on while the rest of the Toa held back the Barraki and their armies. The battle that followed was intense and it seemed certain the Toa would lose. Jaller actually prepared to unleash a nova blast of heat and flame which would have wiped out the Barraki, their forces, and the four Toa beside him as a last-ditch effort to give Matoro the time he needed. At the very last moment, Matoro used the power of the Mask of Life to teleport the Toa Mahri back to Metru Nui. Jaller was able to contain his power so that the city was not destroyed.

As a Toa Mahri, Jaller wore the Kanohi Arthron, the Mask of Sonar. He carried a Cordak blaster and an aquatic power blade. For a brief time, he was assisted by a Hahnah crab.

TOA MAHRI HEWKII

The very last place a Toa of Stone wants to be is underwater. Despite this, Toa Hewkii scored more than his share of victories while in the Pit, helping to save his fellow Toa Mahri and pave the way for the revival of Mata Nui.

Among Hewkii's great deeds as a Toa Mahri were twice defeating a 300-foot long venom eel; battling the ferocious Gadunka; and overcoming an entire school of Takea sharks to stop them from pursuing Matoro.

When Jaller was about to go nova and destroy both the Barraki and the Toa Mahri, Hewkii began to protest. Then he backed off, realizing that it was the only thing to do, and that sometimes being the leader meant making tough choices. Fortunately, the actions of Toa Matoro saved the entire team and the universe.

As a Toa Mahri, Hewkii wore the Kanohi Garai, the Mask of Gravity. He carried a Cordak blaster and an aqua warblade.

TOA MAHRI KONGU

The battle in the Pit was not an easy one for Toa Kongu. His new mask power frightened him, since he never knew what creature he might summon with it (his efforts resulted in a horde of eels suddenly appearing one time, and a primitive, ancient sea beast rising out of the ocean floor another).

Kongu was also the only Toa Mahri to suffer an energy-draining sea squid attack. He was saved by Idler's Hahnah crab, a fact so embarrassing he refuses to discuss it to this day. When the Toa Mahri found the Cordak blasters, Kongu decided to abandon his melee weapon and take two. Asked why he wanted dual blasters, he responded, "Two hands."

Toa Kongu was grief-stricken over Matoro's death, but kept his feelings largely to himself. After the memorial, he took Matoran Chronicler Kopeke aside and warned him that he had "better deep-carve only nice things" about the deceased Toa of Ice.

As a Toa Mahri, Kongu wore the Kanohi Zatth, the Mask of Summoning, which could bring forth sea creatures to aid him. He carried two Cordak blasters.

TOA MAHRI NUPARU

During the battle beneath the sea, Nuparu teamed with Hewkii to search for the Mask of Life. They stumbled on an eel nest and were ambushed and captured by Ehlek. Nuparu used his power to create a pillar of earth to lift them out of their prison, while the two Toa fired Cordak blasters at the monstrous eels who menaced them. During the battle, Hewkii used his mask to make it appear sharks were attacking the eels. This led to a later conflict between Pridak and Ehlek.

Nuparu participated in the major battles with Barraki, the severing of the cord linking Voya Nui to Mahri Nui, and the desperate attempt to buy time for Matoro to save the universe. After the Toa Mahri were teleported back to Metru Nui, he was the first to notice that Matoro was not among them.

Nuparu gave the eulogy for Matoro at the memorial service held in the Metru Nui Coliseum. He and Hewkii later worked together on a carved statue to honor their fallen friend.

As a Toa Mahri, Nuparu wore the Kanohi Volitak, the Mask of Stealth, and carried a Cordak blaster and a shield.

MAHRI NUI

During the centuries that Voya Nui floated on the endless ocean, lava from Mount Valmai cooled in the waters and formed a new land mass. The Matoran built a village upon it which they named Mahri Nui. But the land was unstable. Hundreds of years later, it broke off Voya Nui and sank into the ocean. It plunged down, landing atop a Barraki fortress and destroying it. The villagers were saved by the discovery of air bubbles which enabled them to breathe.

Over time, the surviving Matoran created much larger air bubbles to protect their buildings. They fashioned weapons that launched air spheres to drive away hostile sea creatures. The shock of the sinking had made the Matoran forget about the existence of Voya Nui, so even as cooling lava formed a cord between the two places, the residents of Mahri Nui had no idea home was so near.

...E CORD

...narrow stone structure that linked
...ahri Nui to Voya Nui. It was formed by
...oling lava from Mount Valmai and
...used Mahri Nui to act as an anchor
... the larger island. The Toa Inika
...rneyed down through the cord to
...ch Mahri Nui and later used Cordak
...sters to sever it.

...QUID CAVE

...s was the breeding ground for the
...adly squid used by the Barraki as
...apons. Here Kalmah watched over
... hatchery and saw to it that the squid
...re raised in such a way that their
...tural ferocity would be increased.

...LLARS OF SALT

...tural formation to the north of the
...age, and favorite hunting grounds of
...dak. The Barraki leader brought
...filak there, and both witnessed the
...pearance of a 300-foot venom eel
...m that vantage point.

...ATORAN COUNCIL CHAMBER

...massive chamber located inside the
...hri Nui fortress. Here the goverment
... Mahri Nui met and items that drifted
...wn from the surface were stored.

...ELDS OF AIR

... area adjacent to Mahri Nui where
...weed grew. These precious plants
...oduced air bubbles naturally, which
...uld be harvested using creatures
...led hydruka. The air bubbles allowed
... Mahri Nui Matoran to survive in the
... and protected them from being
...tated by the waters. Carapar briefly
...upied the fields of air with an army
...keras crabs.

...E BLACK WATER

...e ocean below Mahri Nui was
...nsidered to be highly dangerous,
...abited as it was by the Barraki and
...ir armies of sea creatures. Defilak
... an expedition down to these waters,
...ich was wrecked by Pridak and his
...ion of Takea sharks.

Defilak

Dekar

Hydruka Thulox

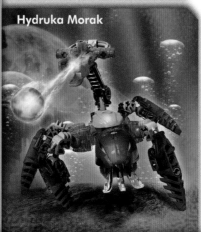
Hydruka Morak

The Mahri Nui Matoran were survivors. They had learned how to take care of themselves and protect themselves in a hostile environment. They knew to wait for the "safe hour," when no predators were around, to tend the fields of air. They even befriended strange beasts called hydruka, who harvested the air bubbles for them.

But nothing could prepare them for what lurked in the black water down below. The Barraki had made this area their new home and both resented the intrusion of the Matoran and saw them as prey. The Matoran defended themselves as best they could, but in the end, what saved their lives was the fact that the Barraki were in no rush to destroy them.

When the Toa Mahri first appeared, the Mahri Nui Matoran attacked them, believing them to be more prisoners of the Pit. Eventually, Toa Hahli was able to convince the village leader, Defilak, that the heroes were friends. Meanwhile, a Po-Matoran hunter named Dekar had found the Mask of Life and run off with it, intending to destroy it. (The Barraki would eventually take the mask away from him.)

During their adventure, the Toa learned that to achieve their mission, they had to sever the stone cord that linked Mahri Nui and Voya Nui. This would almost certainly result in the destruction of the underwater village. They evacuated the Matoran up the cord, where they were met by Axonn. He vowed to keep the Matoran safe no matter what might come next.

The reunion between the Matoran of the two islands was joyful. The Voya Nui Matoran had thought their friends long dead, so seeing them again seemed like a good omen for the future. Axonn took the Matoran down to underground caves where they could survive almost anything.

When the cord was cut, Voya Nui plunged beneath the sea and destroyed Mahri Nui as it passed. It returned to its original place on the southern continent. Once it was settled, the Matoran came out of their caves and began rebuilding their villages under the protection of Axonn.

Pridak

THE BARRAKI

The Barraki were once rulers of six kingdoms that included almost all th
known universe. They formed a League and controlled vast territories wi
their armies. Eventually, they rebelled against the Great Spirit Mata Nu
Their attempt was crushed by a Brotherhood of Makuta army led by Terida

The Barraki were condemned to the Pit, but escaped 1000 years ag
Mutated by the waters into monstrous creatures, they formed new armi
made up of squid, sharks, and other sea beasts. When the Mask of Li
drifted down into the ocean, the Barraki planned to seize it as a means
escape from the Pit.

Some of the important inhabitants of the ocean around Mahri Nui includ

PRIDAK

Former leader of the League of Six Kingdoms and current leader of th
Barraki, Pridak began life in the service of the Brotherhood of Makut
Ambitious, he rapidly tired of serving the Makuta and wished to strike o
on his own. He fought his way to become the leader of a kingdom in th
northeastern section of the universe. Pridak retained his leadership of th
Barraki after their escape from prison. He led the search for the Mask
Life, though his plans were disrupted by a rebellion in the ranks sparked
Ehlek. With the Mask of Life now far out of reach, Pridak remains trappe
in the Pit, with no hope of ever becoming an air-breather again
reclaiming his kingdom. Pridak's primary weapons were a shark too
blade and a squid launcher, and his teeth were strong enough to bi
through protosteel.

Takadox

TAKADOX

Takadox was a sneaky, treacherous villain, always out for himself a
trying to use others. He betrayed the League to the Brotherhood 80,00
years ago, thinking he would go free, but wound up trapped in the
instead. Once he had escaped from prison, he formed an army
undersea insect life and used his hypnotic power to force Carapar to do
bidding. During the struggle for the Mask of Life, he tried to hypnoti
Makuta Teridax. The Makuta used his mental powers to temporarily bre
Takadox's mind. He carried a squid launcher and a pair of knives. He w
part of Brutaka's team sent to rescue Makuta Miserix, but betrayed th
group. His whereabouts are currently unknown.

Ehlek

NOCTURN

A lieutenant of Ehlek's,
Nocturn was very strong
and very stupid. Entrusted
by the Barraki to keep the
Mask of Life safe, he
instead wandered off with
it and lost it to Hydraxon.
Nocturn carried two
swords and a squid
launcher, had incredible
strength, and was im-
mune to the mutagen in
the water. Recaptured by
Hydraxon, he died trying
to make one more
attempt at escape.

Nocturn

EHLEK

The most mysterious of the Barraki, Ehlek was also the only one whose species was native to under the sea. His alien nature always made him feel set apart from the other Barraki. Ehlek constructed a fortress for the Barraki after they escaped from their prison. This was destroyed when Mahri Nui sank and landed on top of it. Ehlek vowed revenge on the Matoran and frequently hunted them for sport. This Barraki carried a squid launcher and was capable of producing electric bolts to jolt his enemies. He has since been recaptured by Hydraxon and imprisoned.

Mantax

MANTAX

One of the six Barraki, Mantax claimed to have no friends, only enemies he had not killed yet. He was convinced that the Barraki rebellion had failed because one of their number had betrayed them, and spent years after their escape from jail trying to prove that. Mantax formed a brief alliance with Hahli and later stole the Mask of Life for himself. He offered to share its power with the other Barraki if they would kill the traitor among them. Mantax carried a squid launcher and his head spikes were coated with a paralyzing venom. He led a large army of manta rays. He remains exiled to the Pit.

CARAPAR

The strongest member of the Barraki, Carapar was brutal and violent. He led an army of fierce crabs and used his powerful pincer to squeeze his enemies until they begged to surrender. Carapar was frequently hypnotized by Takadox, which over time affected his ability to think clearly. In the past, he had been quite a clever conqueror, once capturing a village by giving the residents poisoned food as a "peace gift." Carapar carried a squid launcher. He was forced by Brutaka to join a strike team sent to free Makuta Miserix. He was killed by the ancient entity Tren Krom.

Carapar

KALMAH

Three eyed (one blind), squid like member of the Barraki, Kalmah was the one who discovered the squid cave and realized the potential of the energy draining creatures as weapons. He built the squid launchers used by the Barraki against the Matoran and Toa Mahri. Cool-headed and calculating, Kalmah was ruthless in getting what he wanted. He had no loyalty to Pridak, at one point offering Toa Jaller an alliance if Jaller would kill the Barraki's leader. Kalmah was stranded in the Pit when Toa Matoro escaped with the Mask of Life. He has since been recaptured by Hydraxon and jailed.

Gadunka

GADUNKA

Originally a tiny sea creature, Gadunka was accidentally exposed to the power of the Mask of Life, with both his size and strength vastly increasing. It went on a rampage, battling Toa Hewkii and trying to claim the mask.

Gadunka's major natural weapons were its long, sharp teeth. The Mask of Life later reversed what it had done and shrank Gadunka back to what it had been. It was later eaten by a Takea shark.

Kalmah

MAKUTA'S DIARY

I ONCE TOLD MY ASSEMBLED BROTHERS THAT THERE ARE TIMES ONE CAN ONLY WIN BY LOSING... OR, AT LEAST, APPEARING TO LOSE. ANYONE WHO HAD BEEN PRESENT DURING THE FINAL BATTLE BETWEEN AXONN AND BRUTAKA WOULD HAVE THOUGHT I HAD BEEN DEFEATED. THE VAT HOLDING MY ESSENCE HAD BEEN SHATTERED BY AXONN'S AXE, LEAVING ME WITHOUT A BODY AGAIN. AND THE MASK OF LIFE WAS IN THE DEEP OCEAN, SEEMINGLY OUT OF MY REACH.

NATURALLY, ANYONE WHO THOUGHT THAT WOULD HAVE BEEN WRONG. BUT THEN, YOU KNOW THAT ALREADY, DON'T YOU? BY NOW YOU KNOW THAT HAD I TRULY WANTED THE MASK OF LIFE, NOTHING WOULD HAVE STOPPED MY GETTING IT. BUT I DIDN'T WANT IT – I SIMPLY WANTED TO CONTROL WHEN AND HOW THE TOA MAHRI GOT THEIR HANDS ON IT.

I COULD NOT LET THEM KNOW THAT, OF COURSE, SO I BEHAVED AS THEY EXPECTED ME TO. I POSSESSED THE BODY OF TOA INIKA MATORO TO SOW CONFUSION AND DOUBT AMONG THEM, THEN ALLOWED MYSELF TO BE FORCED OUT OF THAT BODY. I MOVED TO THE ARMORED SHELL OF A MAXILOS ROBOT, TAUNTING MATORO BY LETTING HIM KNOW I WAS THERE. I EVEN ENLISTED HIS HELP IN A RIDICULOUS SCHEME TO HARVEST THE FRAGMENTS OF THE NUI STONE FROM THE REMAINS OF THE LATE TOA TUYET – A MARVELOUS DIVERSION, IF I DO SAY SO MYSELF.

I MUST CONFESS TO FINDING MAHRI NUI A MOST INTERESTING PLACE. WHERE ELSE CAN ONE FIND A HEAVILY ARMED JAILER WHO WAS A MATORAN THE DAY BEFORE, AND HAS NO MEMORY OF IT? AND THE BARRAKI – 80,000 YEARS LATER, THE SAME BRUTAL BUNGLERS, WHOSE PLANS HAD THE SAME DELICATE TOUCH AS A RAMPAGING TAHTORAK. HOW AMUSING IT WAS TO WATCH THEM FIGHT PITCHED BATTLES OVER THE MASK, SCHEMING AGAINST AND BETRAYING EACH OTHER.

(THAT IS NOT SOMETHING THAT WILL EVER HAPPEN AMONG MY ALLIES. ONLY ONE WILL MATTERS: MINE. ONLY ONE VOICE CAN BE HEARD: MINE. ONLY ONE FIST HOLDS THE UNIVERSE IN ITS GRASP: MINE.)

HAVING WON IN THE END, I CAN AFFORD TO ADMIT THAT ALL DID NOT GO AS SMOOTHLY AS I MIGHT HAVE WISHED. THE PATHETIC ATTEMPT BY KARZAHNI TO STAKE A CLAIM TO POWER WAS AN ANNOYANCE, AND HIS EFFORTS TO FRIGHTEN ME WITH VISIONS OF MY POSSIBLE FUTURE A JOKE. I REACHED INTO HIS MIND AND TORE AT IT UNTIL HE SAW HIMSELF FOR WHAT HE WAS... A SIGHT HE COULD NOT STAND, AS IT TURNED OUT.

I HAD ORDERED ONE OF MY BROTHERS TO BRING TO ME AN ARTIFACT CALLED THE STAFF OF ARTAKHA. MY STATED REASON WAS THAT I WISHED TO USE IT TO RE-STORE THE NUI STONE. IN FACT, I SIMPLY WANTED TO STUDY IT. ANYTHING THAT POWERFUL WITH THAT SORT OF POTENTIAL FOR CREATION COULD ALSO BE TURNED INTO AN INCREDIBLE WEAPON OF DESTRUCTION. HE DID BRING IT... BUT I DID NOT GET TO KEEP IT.

BRUTAKA CHOSE THAT MOMENT TO DECIDE TO BE A HERO AGAIN. HE STOLE THE STAFF FROM ME, AND BE-FORE I COULD GET IT BACK, HE HAD PASSED IT ON TO ANOTHER WITH THE ABILITY TO TELEPORT. JUST THAT QUICKLY, THE STAFF WAS GONE FROM THE OCEAN TO I KNEW NOT WHERE.

I TURNED ON BRUTAKA, PREPARED TO DESTROY HIM FOR INTERFERING. HE WAS A FORMIDABLE FOE, AND FOUGHT WITH THE RECKLESS COURAGE OF SOMEONE WHO HAS NOTHING TO LOSE. BUT EVEN WITH THAT, I WOULD HAVE EASILY WON IN THE END, HAD IT NOT BEEN FOR ONE FACT HE SHARED WITH ME. THE BEING CALLING HIMSELF HYDRAXON HAD TAKEN THE MASK AND INTENDED TO DESTROY IT.

THIS COULD NOT BE. IF THE MASK WERE SMASHED, THERE WOULD BE NO WAY TO RESTORE LIFE TO MATA NUI IF HE SHOULD DIE. THE UNIVERSE WOULD COLLAPSE AND I WOULD BE LEFT THE RULER OF ASHES. I NEEDED THAT MASK FAR MORE THAN I NEEDED THE JOY OF CRUSHING BRUTAKA. SO I LEFT HIM THERE, WITH A VOW THAT WE WOULD ONE DAY MEET AGAIN, AND WENT TO SEEK OUT THE MASK AND MAKE SURE IT WOUND UP IN THE HANDS OF THE TOA.

NATURALLY, I COULD NOT SUDDENLY START ACTING LIKE THEIR ALLY. I HAD TO MAKE A SHOW OF TRYING TO TAKE THE MASK AWAY FROM JALLER. BUT WHEN HE PASSED IT ON TO MATORO, I SMILED INSIDE. MY PLAN WAS PROCEEDING. THE ONLY POSSIBLE FLAW WAS THE BARRAKI, WHO MIGHT TAKE THE MASK BACK OR IN SOME OTHER WAY INTERFERE WITH MY TIMING. SO I CHALLENGED THEM, REVEALING MY TRUE IDENTITY, AND PROVIDING THE TOA WITH THE TIME THEY NEEDED TO SEVER THE CORD. THEN I LET THE BARRAKI "DESTROY ME," SO THEY WOULD BE FREE TO DELAY THE TOA JUST ENOUGH FOR MY PURPOSES.

Botar

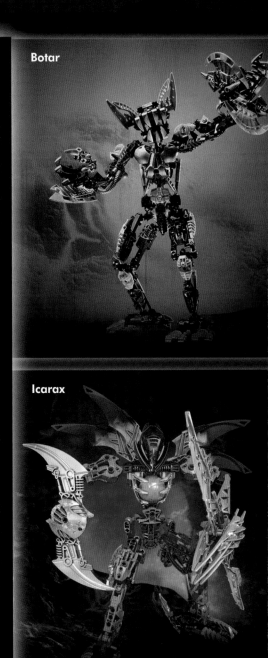

Icarax

Brutaka

THE TOA NUVA'S JOURNE[Y]

Following their rescue on Voy[a] Nui, the Toa Nuva were given [a] mission by the Order of Mata Nu[i]. They were to return to Metru Nu[i] and go to the Great Temple. Ther[e] they would find a scroll detailin[g] what they had to do to prepare th[e] universe for the return of Mata Nu[i] to consciousness. Their tasks in[-] cluded:

1) Freeing the Bahrag so that th[e] Bohrok could be unleashed t[o] clean off the island of Mata Nu[i].

2) Retrieve the Staff of Artakh[a], which could be used to repai[r] the damage done by th[e] massive earthquake 1000 year[s] before. (The Nuva failed in thi[s] task, but the Staff was obtaine[d] by Brutaka.)

3) Retrieve the Heart of th[e] Visorak, an artifact that coul[d] summon the Visorak hord[e] from wherever they might be [–] accomplished by Onua Nuv[a] and Pohatu Nuva.

4) Stop a massive volcanic erup[-] tion on the island of Artidax [–] accomplished by Tahu Nuv[a] and Kopaka Nuva.

5) Track the movements of the re[d] star in the skies above th[e] island of Mata Nui – accom[-] plished by Gali Nuva, who wa[s] startled to discover there wer[e] beings living inside the star.

Lewa Nuva was also dispatched t[o] Mata Nui to obtain a huge sundi[al] that had been buried there. Thi[s] sundial was reduced in size by th[e] Order using a shrink disk and wa[s] later given to Takanuva. By shinin[g] his light upon it, he could create [a] shadow that would point in th[e] direction of the Karda Nui Codrex[.]

When the Toa Nuva had accom[-] plished their tasks, they wer[e] teleported to the island of Artakh[a] to get their next mission.

With the Maxilos robot demolished, the Barraki turned their attention to the Toa Mahri once again. The Toa had the Mask of Life, the one thing the Barraki were sure could turn them into air-breathers again. That would be the first step toward reclaiming the kingdoms they had lost 80,000 years before. So they gathered their armies and pursued the Toa.

With Matoro leading the way, the Toa Mahri were chasing the island of Voya Nui as it flew through the sea back to its origin spot. Harried by the Barraki, they could not move fast enough. The Great Spirit died. But Matoro refused to give up. Jaller told him to go on and make one last attempt to make things right. He and the other Toa Mahri would make a stand and try to hold off the Barraki.

Badly outnumbered, the Toa had no chance, but they fought on anyway. Matoro raced after Voya Nui, managing to follow it through a hole in the sea floor. Down below was the gap once filled by the land mass, and below that, the core of the universe. Straining, Matoro slipped through the gap before the island slammed down on it. The Toa of Ice found himself falling through a vast cavern.

Meanwhile, the Toa were fighting a losing battle. Convinced it was the only way to give Matoro the time he needed, Jaller prepared to unleash a nova blast which would have killed the Barraki, their armies, and the Toa.

In the core, Matoro put on the Mask of Life. The power of that mask began converting his body to energy. Matoro realized that the price of saving Mata Nui's life would be his own. He would become one with the mask and their combined energies would save the Great Spirit. Matoro did not panic or feel any regret. He accepted that this was his destiny and that his sacrifice would save the universe and everyone he cared for.

With this last conscious thought, Matoro used the power of the mask to teleport the other five Toa Mahri back to Metru Nui. With the mask gone, the Barraki were left stranded in the ocean with no way to escape. Matoro let go then, becoming fully energy, and in a great flash of light and life power, Mata Nui was saved!

Gadunka attacks

Toa Mahri Kongu

* * *

Death of a Hero

Toa Matoro dons the Mask of Life as he falls through the core of the universe...

Images flashed through Matoro's mind. He saw the creation of the Ignika; its millennia of waiting for the proper time to be used and the destined wearer; he saw it taken from its resting place once before, to be used to heal the Great Spirit... and he saw what happened to the one who wore it then.

He didn't cry out, or protest, or rush to tear the mask from his face. Nor did he waste a single moment in regret. He had never asked to become a Toa, or desired it, and the mantle of hero had never fit comfortably on his shoulders. But now, now he knew, and the knowledge brought peace.

Nuju was right. The universe is a riddle. And today, I am the answer.

His arms were thrust out in front of him. They were glowing now, little sparkles of light like the starfield above the island of Mata Nui. His whole body was changing now, patterns of light swirling, energies being unleashed, as the Mask of Life drew forth the essence of the being called Matoro.

Is this the end then? he wondered. *Is this what it feels like?*

Yes, he decided. *This was death.*

This was the price the Ignika demanded for its use. He would no longer exist as Matoro, as a Toa, as a living being of organic muscle and mechanical parts... he would be far less than what he was, and far more.

The world was changing all around him, but it did not frighten the Toa of Ice. He knew the real change was in how he was viewing his surroundings – no longer with eyes, a mind, a spirit bound to the physical world. He was becoming pure energy, pure life... the force that would bring the Great Spirit back from death. Already, he could barely remember how it felt to be in battle, or to be lonely, or to feel the warmth of a fire on a cold night. Pleasure, pain, satisfaction, disappointment, these were all just words to him now. He was beyond all that, or almost.

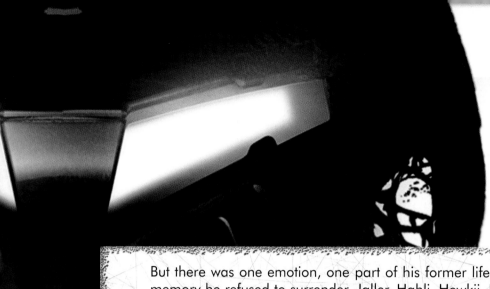

But there was one emotion, one part of his former life, that he had not forgotten – on[e] memory he refused to surrender. Jaller, Hahli, Hewkii, Kongu, Nuparu – his friends – hi[s] partners – who had fought beside him and laughed with him and made all the burden[s] bearable. They were out there now in the black water, about to die at the claws of th[e] Barraki. No one on Metru Nui would ever know of their heroism or the sacrifices they wer[e] willing to make. They would never see their homes or those they cared about ever again[.]

His own death, he could accept – but theirs? No, that was too high a price to pay, even t[o] buy the salvation of a universe.

He was Toa Matoro, at least for a few moments more, and he wore the Mask of Life. O[r] perhaps the Mask of Life now wore him. He didn't know, or care. He knew his friends wer[e] willing to die for him and his destiny, and for that reason alone, they had to live.

Matoro pushed back against the power of the mask, fighting to hold on to hi[s] consciousness and his own existence for just another heartbeat. He wrestled with the powe[r,] pleaded with it, tried to bend it to his will. The Ignika, for reasons of its own, allowed this[.]

Once before, long ago, a Toa had donned the Ignika and lost his life to complete hi[s] mission. That Toa had tried to be brave, but there was fear in his heart and he met his en[d] with grief and regret. The Ignika sensed none of this in Matoro – only a will an[d] determination that rivaled even that of Mata Nui himself.

The Mask of Life, bound now to the energy of Matoro, granted him its power. Matoro seize[d] upon it to perform his final act. It was not one of grand heroism, not a gesture that woul[d] shake the universe, but something more powerful and lasting than either one: a simple a[ct] of friendship.

With that done, Matoro surrendered himself gratefully and completely to his destiny. Th[e] merged energies of Toa and Kanohi mask exploded in the core of the universe, floodin[g] it with light. Streams of golden power flowed into every part of this realm and then beyon[d] it, until it had touched every place where the Great Spirit had once reigned. Just a[s] countless beings had sensed the death of Mata Nui, so did they now feel life return to him[.] And in the sky above the city of Metru Nui, the stars shone brightly once more…

* * *

In the core of the universe, the Matoran of Karda Nui are under attack by a trio of Makut[a] *when Matoro's sacrifice takes the form of an explosion of light and energy … one s[o]* *powerful it blinds the Makuta.*

Then came the light, brilliant, blinding – it seeped through solid stone, through walls an[d] roof and hatch, illuminating the entire chamber. It was as if a trillion lightstones had bee[n] turned on all at once … on second thought, that would have seemed like a dim glo[w] compared to the radiance that filled the chamber, and all of Karda Nui. It lasted an instant, and it lasted forever. Each and every Matoran felt a surge of hope as bright as the light had been, as if some measure of balance had suddenly been restored to the universe.

Tanma suddenly realized he had closed his eyes. The light had been so bright that it had made no difference. Opening them, he checked to make sure everyone was all right. Satisfied that they were, he went to the hatch, opened it, and peeked out.

The three Makuta were still in the air, but something had changed. They no longer flew straight and true, but wheeled crazily through the sky. There was a faint glow attached to everything, as if an inferno had raged a moment before and then been extinguished, leaving burning embers behind.

"What is it? What do you see out there?" asked Photok.

Tanma took a long time to answer. When he did, it was to say, "I really don't know. Maybe it's the start of something… or maybe the end of everything."

* * *

Meanwhile, the Toa Nuva are being given a new mission and new armor by the mysterious Artakha…

"You have done all that has been asked of you, and more," said Artakha. "You have earned this armor. Wear it well, for it is perhaps my greatest creation. Wherever you journey, it will adapt to your surroundings. No terrain, no climate, no wind or wave will ever again be your master."

"Now you must leave here. The time has come at last for the Great Spirit Mata Nui to awaken – and you must be the ones to bring him back to those who need him."

"Wait!" said Tahu Nuva. "Let us see you!"

"Come with us!" said Onua Nuva, Toa of Earth. "Your aid would be welcome, Artakha."

"No," said Artakha, even as the Toa Nuva's vision began to blur. "Where you travel, you must travel alone."

A moment later, the island of Artakha was gone – or so it seemed. In fact, the Toa Nuva had been transported from the island by the power of its ruler. When their vision finally cleared, they were in mid-air, high above a strange Matoran village. Somehow, their armor had shifted in a hundred ways, making it possible for them to stay aloft. But there was no time to wonder about that – all around them, a battle raged in the sky.

* * *

After the cataclysmic earthquake that shook the universe 1000 years ago, great stalactites broke off from the ceiling of Karda Nui and buried themselves in the ground. Matoran of Light, displaced from their homes by the quake, built villages atop the upturned bases of the stalactites. These villages were linked to each other by vine bridges. Transport between villages was also accomplished by means of flight packs worn by the Matoran. After the Makuta invasion, some of the villages were protected by lightvines, luminescent plant life from the swamp below.

THE HIVE

When the Makuta came to Karda Nui, they created a hive for themselves which hung from the ceiling of the huge cave. Inside, Antroz, Vamprah, Chirox and Mutran would gather for strategy sessions. The hive was also the site of the vats in which shadow leeches were created. Mutran and his assistant Vican did most of this work and also served as guardians for the hive. The Toa Nuva invaded the hive and were captured, but escaped thanks to Pohatu Nuva. They later destroyed the hive, forcing Mutran to move his operations to the swamp.

THE SWAMP

When the earthquake struck, water from outside of the domed universe flooded into Karda Nui, turning the ground into a vast swamp. The murky waters were mutagenic, transforming any living thing that came in contact with them. Strange plant life grew here as well, all of it twisted, some of it dangerous. The three Makuta who were exposed to the swamp waters were mutated by them and lost their ability to shapeshift. The Toa Nuva journeyed to the swamp to find keystones that would allow them to enter the Codrex and to search for the Mask of Life. Major battles also took place here between the Toa and the Makuta. The swamp was destroyed by the energy storm that struck Karda Nui.

THE CODREX

A mysterious spherical structure in the swamp of Karda Nui, the Codrex has a long history. It was built by the Great Beings and served three purposes:

• housing the Axalara T9, Rockoh T3 and Jetrax T6 vehicles,
• providing shelter and protection to the Toa Mata in their Toa canisters,
• containing the technology necessary to awaken Mata Nui should that become necessary.

The Toa Nuva rediscovered the Codrex when they returned to Karda Nui. It could be opened only by the use of six keystones. Inside, it seemed vastly bigger than it did on the outside. The use of a bank of machinery opened a portal in the floor which led to the resting place of the vehicles and the power core used to awaken Mata Nui. Antroz followed the Toa into this area and stole the Jetrax T6. Ignika sacrificed its existence as Toa here to revive the Great Spirit. The Codrex still stands in Karda Nui, having survived the attacks of the Makuta and

MAKUTA'S DIARY

AH, HOW STRANGE IT IS, NOW THAT I HAVE ACHIEVED ULTIMATE POWER, TO LOOK BACK ON THE MAKUTA I WAS. IT HAS BEEN A LONG JOURNEY FROM OVERSEEING METRU NUI TO EMBODYING THE UNIVERSE, BUT THE END HAS MADE IT WORTH EVERY MOMENT'S TRIAL.

I CANNOT RECALL JUST WHEN IT WAS THAT I GREW DISSATISFIED WITH MY EXISTENCE. I KNOW THAT I HAD ALWAYS FOUND IT TROUBLING THAT THE MATORAN WOULD FALL ALL OVER THEMSELVES TO HONOR MATA NUI, YET IGNORE MYSELF AND MY BROTHERS. HAD WE NOT CREATED THE RAHI THEY USED EACH DAY IN THEIR LABOURS? DID WE NOT PROTECT THEM FROM THEMSELVES? AND WHERE WAS MATA NUI? KEEPING THE STARS IN THE SKY, MAKING THE SUNS RISE, WITH NO IDEA WHAT HIS PEOPLE WERE UP TO AT ANY GIVEN TIME.

AFTER MY GLORIOUS DEFEAT OF THE BARRAKI, I BEGAN TO PONDER IF OVERTHROWING THE GREAT SPIRIT MIGHT BE POSSIBLE. IT WAS NUTRAN WHO SHOWED ME THAT IT COULD BE DONE, BUT IT WOULD TAKE A BEING OF GREAT SKILL AND DARING TO ACHIEVE IT. I KNEW I WAS THAT BEING.

AT FIRST, OF COURSE, MY AMBITIONS WERE SMALL. I SOUGHT ONLY TO DISABLE MATA NUI AND SHOW THE MATORAN WHO THEY SHOULD TRULY BE WORSHIPPING. I PROPOSED THIS PLAN TO MY BROTHERS, BUT AS I EXPECTED, MAKUTA MISERIX REFUSED TO AGREE TO MY IDEA. I KNEW IT WAS TIME TO TAKE THE FINAL STEP. I CHALLENGED MISERIX'S LEADERSHIP AND OTHERS STOOD WITH ME. HE WAS FORCED FROM POWER AND I TOOK OVER LEADERSHIP OF THE BROTHERHOOD.

MY FIRST COMMAND WAS MISERIX'S EXECUTION, ALONG WITH THOSE OF THE MAKUTA WHO HAD SUPPORTED HIM. IT WAS ONLY LATER I WOULD LEARN THAT KRIKA HAD DISOBEYED ME AND MERELY IMPRISONED MISERIX ON THE ISLAND OF ARTIDAX.

WITH THAT DONE, I SET TO WORK CRAFTING THE VIRUS THAT WOULD SEND MATA NUI INTO AN UNENDING SLEEP. AT THE SAME TIME, I ACTED TO REMOVE POTENTIAL THREATS, SUCH AS THE MASK OF LIGHT CREATED ON ARTAKHA. I SLOWLY AND QUIETLY MUSTERED AN ARMY OF RAHKSHI, VISORAK AND EXO-TOA, AND PUT THE DARK HUNTERS TO WORK ELIMINATING TOA AND TURAGA AROUND THE UNIVERSE.

THE MAKUTA

The Makuta were created by the Great Spirit Mata Nui to aid him in protecting and maintaining the Matoran universe. Specifically, their job was to create Rahi beasts that would play useful roles in the operation of the universe. This they did by mixing viruses with liquid protodermis, creating every known creature that walks, flies, or swims.

Originally, the members of the Brotherhood of Makuta were bio-mechanical – a combination of organic tissue and mechanical parts, much like Toa or Matoran. But over time, the Makuta evolved. Their muscle and tissue turned to pure energy, which they housed in protosteel armor. Although the energy could dissipate if outside of a body too long, the change made the Makuta much more difficult to physically harm.

Mata Nui had gifted the Makuta with a number of powers, including the control of the shadow element. Although shadow is a dangerous element, Mata Nui knew there would need to be some Rahi who dwelled in darkness, and the Makuta would need to be able to master that darkness to control them. He also made the Makuta shapeshifters, again to make them better able to master the Rahi they created.

After the Matoran civil war, the Makuta's roles changed. Their leader, Makuta Miserix, decided that one Makuta should be assigned to oversee each region of the universe. The intent was to make sure no more disruptions of the Matoran labors would occur. The Makuta became active in stopping threats to the peace, such as the Barraki rebellion.

…OF MY ADVENTURES ON METRU NUI, MATA NUI, AND VOYA NUI, I HAVE ALREADY WRITTEN. BUT LET ME MAKE IT CLEAR – I KNEW FROM THE BEGINNING MY ACTIONS MIGHT RESULT IN MATA NUI'S DEATH. I PLANNED FOR IT… I ANTICIPATED IT… ONE MIGHT EVEN SAY THAT AT SOME POINT I HOPED FOR IT. I DID NOT NEED HIM DEAD AT LEAST NOT AT THE START – BUT HE HAD OUTLIVED HIS USEFULNESS. HE WAS LIKE ONE OF THOSE PREHISTORIC RAHI SO LOVED BY THE MATORAN, MAVRAH – BIG AND SLOW AND UNFIT FOR SURVIVAL IN THIS MODERN UNIVERSE. TAKING HIS RULE EVEN HIS LIFE, WOULD BE TO SHOW MERCY TO ALL THOSE WHO LIVED HERE. FOR TOO LONG, THEY HAD BEEN DIRECTIONLESS, LOST WITHOUT THEIR GREAT SPIRIT NOW THEY WOULD HAVE PURPOSE AGAIN – AND THAT PURPOSE WOULD BE THE GREATER GLORY OF MAKUTA TERIDAX.

STILL, I COULD PLOT AND PLAN… I COULD TRY TO ANTICIPATE EVERY CONTINGENCY BUT IN THE END, I COULD NOT MAKE THIS PLAN SUCCEED. I HAD TO RELY ON OTHERS. WHAT IS MOST AMAZING IS THAT I HAD TO RELY ON TOA! I HAD TO TRUST IN THEIR NOBILITY, THEIR UNWILLINGNESS TO EVER ADMIT DEFEAT, THEIR ABILITY TO OVERCOME EVERY OBSTACLE, AND THEIR LONG HISTORY OF WINNING OUT, NO MATTER THE ODDS. I NEEDED THE TOA MAHRI AND THE TOA NUVA TO PLAY THEIR PARTS IN THIS DRAMA I HAD CRAFTED… AND IF THEY DID, IT WOULD BE I WHO WOULD FINALLY BRING DOWN THE CURTAIN ON THE LONG REIGN OF THE GREAT SPIRIT MATA NUI.

It was after that rebellion that Makuta Teridax began thinking about seizing power. Putting his plan into motion, he eventually led an attack on Mata Nui that resulted in the Great Spirit falling into an unending sleep. Efforts by him to seize power in Metru Nui and quickly achieve domination of the universe were frustrated by Toa. Despite this, the Makuta remained the major threat to peace and security in this universe.

Although they were incredibly powerful, Makuta did have weaknesses. Being creatures of shadow they were vulnerable to light. If their armor was cracked or damaged, their essence leaked out. They had to then find a new body within a few weeks or cease to exist. In addition, there was what was called the "curse of the Makuta" – their own ambition and lust for power sometimes caused them to make mistakes or underestimate their opponents.

Most Makuta specialized in certain things. Chirox and Mutran, for example, continued to refine their abilities to create Rahi, Icarax focused on mastering combat, Vamprah honed his skills as a hunter and so on.

The Brotherhood's main fortress was located on the island of Destral. The island was capable of being teleported to various locations as needed by the Makuta. It was guarded by Rahkshi, Visorak and Exo-Toa. The fortress of Destral was largely destroyed by an Order of Mata Nui attack.

Only two Makuta have ever been barred from the Brotherhood. The first was Miserix, who was overthrown by Teridax and later reappeared to try to stop the Brotherhood's plans. The second was Spiriah, who was blamed for the failed experiment that resulted in the savage and uncontrollable Skakdi. Spiriah was part of the team that freed Miserix from the island of Artidax.

There are very few Makuta currently still active in the universe. Since Teridax seized complete control, he has seen little need to allow potential rivals to live. The Makuta who do survive are used to mass produce kraata so that Teridax's Rahkshi armies remain strong.

MAKUTA ANTROZ

Antroz was the leader of the Makuta in Karda Nui and one of the Brotherhood's most skilled tactical commanders. He was smart enough not to make the common Makuta mistake of underestimating his foes, and even fought with some sense of honor (a rarity among his species).

He led three other Makuta – Vamprah, Chirox, and Mutran – in attacks on the villages of the Matoran of Light. Their goal was to convert the Matoran into shadow Matoran, thus making it impossible for any more Toa of Light to come into being. They had defeated all but one village when the Toa Nuva arrived in Karda Nui and began to actively oppose them. Antroz's armor was damaged during a battle with Kopaka, but he was able to patch it sufficiently to return to the fight.

When the Toa discovered three powerful vehicles inside the Codrex, Antroz stole one, the Jetrax T6, and battled Lewa Nuva and Pohatu Nuva in the air. Kopaka Nuva eventually seized control of the craft. Antroz later perished in the energy storm unleashed when Mata Nui awoke.

Antroz wore the Kanohi Jutlin, the Mask of Corruption, which could rot any object. He was capable of flight and had claws and poisonous fangs. He also carried a Tridax pod filled with shadow leeches. Due to exposure to the explosion of light that accompanied Mata Nui's return to life, he lost his sight and had to rely on a shadow Matoran, Radiak, to navigate.

RADIAK

Radiak was a warrior and a famous hero among the Av-Matoran. Turned into a shadow Matoran by Vamprah, he proved to be just as fierce a fighter for evil as he had been for good.

When Antroz and Radiak were physically linked, both gained new abilities. Antroz was able to see through Radiak's eyes via a mental link. Radiak was able to slow opponents, making them feel too lazy to act.

Radiak was turned back into a Matoran of Light thanks to the efforts of Takanuva, and now lives on Metru Nui.

MAKUTA CHIROX

A brilliant Makuta, Chirox's Rahi creati
tended to be creatures who were
helpful or benevolent, but destructi
Chirox was the one who discovered that
Makuta had evolved from organic
energy, and that they could now poss
other bodies in this form.

Chirox battled the Toa Nuva both in the s
and in the swamp, while also clashing w
Mutran, his long-time rival among
Makuta. He was also the first to voice
suspicion that Teridax had sent the Mak
to Karda Nui not to achieve a vital missi
but as a way of getting rid of them.

During Takanuva's attempt to rescue
shadow Matoran, Chirox mounted
attack on the Toa of Light. He was ba
beaten by Takanuva and had his arn
pierced by a laser burst. Wounded, he h
to retreat. Chirox was later killed by
energy storm that struck Karda Nui.

Chirox wore the Kanohi Shelek, the Mask
Silence, which could rob an opponent of
senses of speech and hearing. He carrie
pair of hook blades and a Tridax pod fil
with shadow leeches. He was blinded
the explosion of light in Karda Nui and h
to rely on a shadow Matoran to provide h
with sight.

KIROP

Former leader of the Matoran of Light in
Karda Nui, he was transformed into a
shadow Matoran by Chirox. The Toa Nuva
captured him and then purposely let him go
so he would lead them to the hive where
the shadow leeches were created.

When linked to Chirox, Kirop had the
power to temporarily blind an opponent.
Chirox gained the ability to see through
Kirop's eyes as long as they were in contact.

Thanks to Takanuva, Kirop was transformed back into a Matoran of Light. He
now resides on Metru Nui.

MAKUTA VAMPRAH

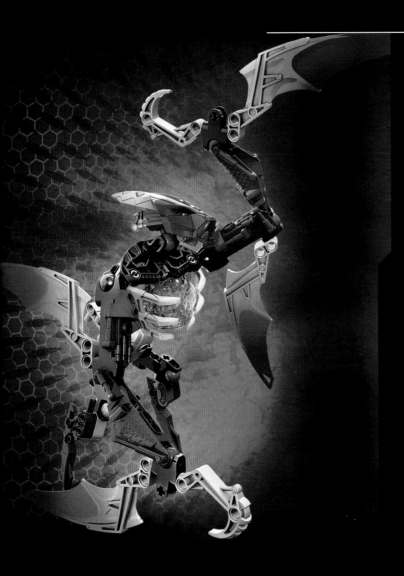

The silent hunter of the Makuta, Vamprah loved to stalk Matoran and use his mask to turn them into shadow versions of themselves. Often, he would allow his prey to temporarily escape, just to prolong the pleasure of the hunt. While capable of speech, Vamprah believed that a good hunter never makes unnecessary noise.

Vamprah was the first Makuta to discover the portal into Karda Nui. Following the battles in the skies of Karda Nui, Vamprah was defeated by Tahu Nuva down in the swamp. He later teamed with Gorast to challenge Icarax, teaming with her to kill the renegade Makuta.

Bitil refused to aid Vamprah to escape Karda Nui when the energy storm erupted. Vamprah perished in the storm, typically without saying a word.

Vamprah wore the Kanohi Avsa, the Mask of Hunger, which was capable of draining energy or light from a target over distance. He used knife-sharp wings and claws in combat and also carried a Tridax pod filled with shadow leeches. He was blinded by the light explosion in Karda Nui and had to rely on a shadow Matoran to provide him with a means of seeing the world around him.

GAVLA

The first Karda Nui Matoran to be transformed into a shadow Matoran and later leader of that group, Gavla had never liked her fellow villagers and so fell easily into the role of opposing them.

When physically linked with Vamprah, she gained the ability to disrupt an opponent's balance. Vamprah was able to see through her eyes when in physical contact with her.

Gavla was transformed back to a Matoran of Light against her will and agreed to travel to Metru Nui only because she saw no other option left to her.

MAKUTA ICARAX

A rebellious Makuta with designs on leadership the Brotherhood, Icarax is also the most highly skil of his species in combat. Shortly after the fall of M Nui, Icarax lost faith in Teridax's leadership c attempted to conquer the universe through for Teridax confronted him and beat him after a ba that lasted for days. While Teridax was in Mahri N he telepathically ordered Icarax to retrieve the M of Shadows and the Staff of Artakha. The quest the latter brought Icarax into conflict with the Nuva and resulted in the destruction of Karzahr realm.

Icarax was summoned by Antroz to Karda Nui battle the Toa Nuva. He almost immediately fou himself in combat with the Toa Ignika, a living be that embodied the power of the Mask of Life. Ign devolved Icarax back into being a bio-mechani being, a process that was quite painful for Makuta.

Icarax later talked Krika into helping him attack Codrex in an effort to frustrate Teridax's ultim plan. Vamprah, Mutran and Gorast attacked him retaliation. He was killed when his teleport abi went wild and he was transported to a milli different places at once.

Makuta Icarax wore the Kanohi Kraahkan, the M of Shadows. He was armed with a rotating shad sword, a shield, and a Tridax pod filled with shad leeches.

MUTRAN AND VICAN

A skilled designer of Rahi, Mutran would play a significant role in the creation of Makuta Teridax's plans. He was sent by Miserix to meet with Tren Krom, the ancient entity who oversaw the universe prior to the coming of Mata Nui. While there, he saw into Tren Krom's mind while that being was reading his and learned much of the nature of the Great Spirit and the universe. This knowledge made the Makuta realize it would be possible to one day overthrow Mata Nui and seize power.

Mutran worked with his rival, Chirox, to create the shadow leeches and Tridax pods. In Karda Nui, Mutran monitored their creation and guarded the hive where they came into being. This hive was later destroyed by the Toa Nuva, forcing Mutran to relocate to the swamp.

While working in his new location, Mutran produced a winged Rahi called a klakk. The klakk escaped, and it was later discovered that its sonic scream could shatter the psychic shield that blocked light from entering a shadow Matoran. Using the klakk's power, Takanuva was able to cure himself and the shadow Matoran.

Mutran aided Gorast and Vamprah in their successful attack on Icarax. When the energy storm struck Karda Nui, Mutran tried to get close and study it. He was incinerated by a bolt of power from the heart of the storm.

Vican was Mutran's shadow Matoran assistant. He was the first to be cured by the klakk and left with the Av-Matoran to travel to Metru Nui.

THE MATORAN OF LIGHT

The Matoran of Light, or Av-Matoran, have a long and rich history. They were the first tribe created by the Great Beings, and as such, they were larger, stronger and more powerful than standard Matoran. Of all villagers, only Av-Matoran are able to harness and use their elemental power in combat.

Shortly after their creation, the Great Beings used the remains of the process to create the first krana. An unintended side effect was the creation of the Zyglak, a race who later proved to be a dangerous menace. Av-Matoran were designed by the Great Beings so that at a certain stage, many of them would go dormant and evolve into the mechanical Bohrok.

The Av-Matoran briefly lived in Karda Nui, prior to the coming of Mata Nui. That was where they first encountered the Toa Mata, who were there to battle a plague of intelligent lightning bolts called avohkah. The Av-Matoran left Karda Nui before the energy storm hit the first time, moving into caverns in the roof above the core.

Some time later, a number of Av-Matoran disappeared. The tribe would never know that they had been taken by the Order of Mata Nui, brainwashed into forgetting they were Av-Matoran, and placed in different geographic areas. This was meant to insure that some Av-Matoran would survive if ever a threat to the main tribe should occur.

When the Great Cataclysm struck, portions of the roof broke off, carrying many Av-Matoran down with them. Massive stalactites impaled in the floor of the core, and flood waters began to spill in, turning the lower level into a swamp. The Av-Matoran created villages on the upturned bases of the stalactites and lived in harmony and peace for more than 1000 years.

A short time ago, their world was invaded by the Brotherhood of Makuta, who began transforming the Matoran of Light into evil shadow Matoran. One village held out, eventually receiving aid from the Toa Nuva. The surviving Av-Matoran teamed with the Toa to do battle with the Makuta and the shadow Matoran.

Knowing the energy storm would strike again as soon as Mata Nui was awakened, Takanuva gathered the Matoran of Light together and saw to it that they were evacuated out of Karda Nui. They made their way to Metru Nui, where they still reside.

Av-Matoran are capable of hurling light bursts from their hands and of changing how the eye perceives light, so that can appear to be other colors beside their native white and gold.

The brave Av-Matoran

TOA NUVA LEWA

Lewa found himself extraordinar‍[y] prepared for the battle in Kard‍[a] Nui, given that he already h‍[ad] experience in flying. Aft‍[er] arriving in the core, he mounte‍[d] a rescue mission for Pohatu ar‍[d] Kopaka with Tanma, battle‍[d] Antroz to a standstill, and helpe‍[d] destroy the shadow leech hive.

Moving down to the swamp‍, Lewa worked with Gali ‍[to] produce a massive thunderstor‍[m] to distract the Makuta. He late‍[r] piloted the Axalara T9 in batt‍[le] against Antroz in the Jetrax ‍[T6] and assorted Makuta. H‍[e] successfully escaped the co‍[re] along with the other Toa and ‍[is] now in Metru Nui.

Lewa's adaptive armor allowe‍[d] him to fly. While in Karda Nui, h‍[e] carried a Midak skyblaster whic‍[h] fired bolts of light and wielded a‍[n] air saber. His Kanohi Miru Nuv‍[a,] the Mask of Levitation, gave hi‍[m] the ability to maneuver bett‍[er] while in flight.

TANMA

Tanma was the leader of the Av-Matoran survivors following the capture of Kirop by the Makuta. He organized the defense of the village during the period before the Toa Nuva's arrival in Karda Nui. Although he did not recognize the Toa, he did immediately act to save Lewa from a shadow leech.

When he accidentally landed on Lewa, they discovered that the physical contact made it possible for Lewa to access Tanma's memories. Tanma, in turn, was able to act as a living energy source for Lewa's skyblaster.

Tanma carried two power swords and wore a rocket booster on his back, which allowed him to fly. He currently lives on Metru Nui.

TOA NUVA POHATU

Flight did not come naturally to a Toa of Stone, but Pohatu knew he had to master combat in the air or die. Despite a number of close calls, including being thrown toward the swamp by Chirox's shadow hand, Pohatu proved to be an effective fighter. Captured along with Kopaka and Lewa and chained up in the Makuta hive, he used his Mask of Speed to escape and free the others before destroying the hive.

Pohatu piloted the Rockoh T3 above the swamp, doing battle with Antroz in the stolen Jetrax T6. Pohatu played a key role in the battle by forming a stone hand that erupted from the muddy waters and held the Jetrax in place while he raked the side of the stolen ship with energy bolts.

In Karda Nui, Pohatu carried twin propellers and a Midak skyblaster. He wore the Kanohi Kakama, the Great Mask of Speed. He is currently back on Metru Nui.

OTOK

aring, risk-taking Av-Matoran, tok teamed with Pohatu Nuva battle with the Makuta. They red a number of dangerous ations, from being plummeted ard the swamp by Icarax's vity power to being trapped ide a giant rock by Gorast. But h time they survived, thanks to ver and sharp wits.

en in physical contact, Pohatu ld share Photok's memories, ething that saved them when y were battling Icarax. (Photok w the location of a fallen actite through which the two uld smash to try and slow their .) Photok gained the power of t speed, so he could add to atu's velocity.

tok carried two power swords wore a rocket booster on his k, which allowed him to fly. He w lives on Metru Nui.

TOA NUVA KOPAKA

The Toa of Ice served as team lead for the squad assigned to protect th Matoran villages in Karda Nui. was not an easy job, as they face five fierce and powerful Makut Relying on his intelligence to se him through, Kopaka masterminde the capture of Kirop and the plan let him escape and follow him ba to the shadow leech hive. This led the destruction of the hive and d great damage to the Makuta ability to produce the leeches.

Kopaka intended to pilot the Jetr T6, but Antroz stole the ship befor he could do so. He later regained and flew it in battle against th Makuta. Later, he prevente Takanuva from succumbing to h dark side and killing Chirox.

On Karda Nui, Kopaka carried Midak skyblaster with a blizza blade attached and a laser targetir system. He also had a targetir system built into his mask. He currently back on Metru Nui.

SOLEK

Solek is an expert on the ancient legends of the Toa Mata and particularly on those of Kopaka. He was overjoyed to see the Nuva arrive and was bursting with questions for them. Unfortunately, the answers had to wait as there were battles to be won against the Makuta.

He teamed with Kopaka Nuva to battle Mutran and later saved a handful of other Av-Matoran. He also participated in the battles against the Makuta in the swamp and aided Takanuva in his round-up of the shadow Matoran.

When in physical contact, Kopaka could share Solek's memories. Solek gained the power to create objects out of solid light. Solek carried two power swords and wore a rocket booster on his back, which allowed him to fly. He now lives on Metru Nui.

The heroes arrive...

BATTLE IN THE SKY

When the Toa Nuva were teleported by Artakha into Karda Nui, they found themselves in the middle of a pitched battle between a trio of Makuta and the Matoran of Light. Although the Makuta were beaten back, the Toa knew it was only a matter of time before they would be back.

Fearing the Makuta might get hold of the Mask of Life, Tahu led Gali and Onua down to the swamp far below. Kopaka and Pohatu were promptly defeated by the enemy, but Lewa and Tanma mounted a successful rescue effort. Meanwhile, Antroz dispatched Vican to the island of Destral to bring back Makuta Icarax to combat the Toa.

The heroes learned much of what had happened in Karda Nui over the past few days – how the Makuta had used shadow leeches to drain the light from Av-Matoran, turning them into evil shadow Matoran. Determined to stop this, the Toa captured Kirop and then let him escape, trailing him back to the shadow leech hive. They were joined by a mysterious new Toa who none of them recognized (Toa Ignika).

Inside the hive, the Toa were tricked into battling Ignika and then captured. Led by Pohatu, they escaped, pausing only to destroy the hive. Makuta Icarax challenged Toa Ignika, but was soundly defeated.

Seeing the battle going against them, the Makuta retreated to the swamp. The Toa Nuva and their Av-Matoran followed, leaving Toa Ignika to guard the fallen Icarax. The Makuta later informed Ignika that the Mask of Life was a threat to all that lived, prompting Ignika to abandon his guard duty to find the Toa Nuva and tell them of the danger.

TOA IGNIKA

After Matoro's death, the Kanohi Ignika, or Mask of Life, fell to the bottom of the Karda Nui swamp. Sensing the presence of hostile forces nearby, it decided to make a body for itself so it could fight if need be. Inspired by Matoro's heroism, it made itself look like a Toa.

Toa Ignika rocketed up to the sky and aided the Toa against the Makuta, easily defeating Icarax. It later learned that if the universe were not brought into balance again, an automatic power built into the mask would extinguish all life in the universe.

Racing against time to awaken Mata Nui, the Toa Nuva turned to Ignika to provide the needed power. Although reluctant to give up his newfound life, Toa Ignika finally sacrificed itself to awaken the Great Spirit.

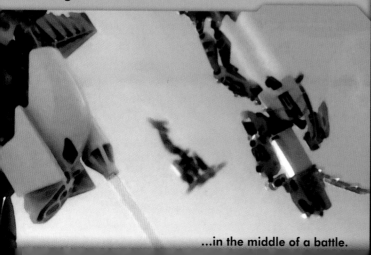

...in the middle of a battle.

73

THE MASK OF LIFE

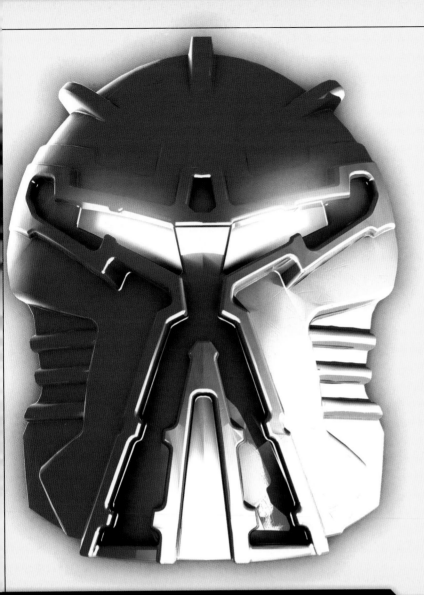

The Kanohi Ignika was created by the Great Beings, with two purposes in mind. The mask could be used to revive the Great Spirit Mata Nui should his life energies ever wane. It could also wipe out all life in the universe should that become necessary, opening the way for new to be created. The mask was gold in color, but would turn silver and then black if its countdown to destruction began.

The mask was hidden on Voya Nui and guarded by sentries such as Umbra, Axonn, and Brutaka. Over the course of 100,000 years, it was taken from its resting place only once. This took place when the Matoran Civil War badly weakened Mata Nui, and a Toa team led by Jovan had to retrieve and use the mask.

To prevent abuse of its power, the mask would curse anyone who touched it when they were not destined to do so. Some examples of its curses were making everything inanimate come to life wherever the afflicted went, giving a victim a death touch, and inflicting madness. The Ignika was also able to evolve or devolve any living being, transform beings completely, teleport them across the universe and more. Along with the Kanohi Vahi, the Mask of Time, it is considered a Legendary mask.

MASKS OF POWER

The Ignika is one of only two known Legendary masks, but there are many powerful masks in existence. Here are some:

KANOHI VAHI – The Mask of Time, created by Toa Vakama, could slow down or speed up time around a target. Its destruction would rip time itself to shreds. The Vahi was used twice, by Vakama against Makuta Teridax and by Tahu Nuva against the Bohrok-Kal. It is currently on Metru Nui.

Kanohi Vahi

KANOHI AVOHKII – The Great Mask of Light, worn by Takanuva, this mask was made by Artakha. It was stolen from him by the Makuta and later retrieved by the Toa Hagah. Donning the mask transformed Takua into the Toa of Light.

KANOHI KRAAHKAN – The Great Mask of Shadows, worn in the past by Makuta Teridax and later Makuta Icarax. It was capable of creating darkness, anger and fear. Its origin is unknown. It was destroyed when Icarax perished.

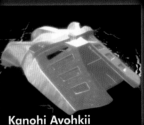

Kanohi Avohkii

KANOHI OLMAK – The Great Mask of Dimensional Gates, worn by Brutaka, allowed the user to open portals to inter-dimensional space. Brutaka used this mask to send Takanuva from Metru Nui to Karda Nui, but damage to the mask resulted in Takanuva winding up in multiple alternate dimensions.

KANOHI RODE – The Great Mask of Truth worn by Axonn. This mask allowed the user to see through any deception or disguise. It also allowed Axonn to see and communicate with Toa Matoro when he was in spirit form.

***

Federation of Fear

The Order of Mata Nui decides to rescue Makuta Miserix, former leader of the Brotherhood, from his imprisonment on Artidax. They hope to use him in their coming war with the Makuta. Brutaka leads a team of condemned villains on this dangerous mission, only to find that Takadox has betrayed them all and tried to bury them in a cave-in...

Brutaka pushed aside a pile of rubble and struggled to his feet. Around him, Spiriah and Roodaka were using shadow energy to blast themselves free. Vezon and Lariska were nowhere to be seen.

He glanced back toward the now blocked tunnel entrance. A few blasts of power would no doubt clear away the pile of rocks and stones, but Takadox would be long gone by now. There would be time to settle with him later.

"I've got him!"

Brutaka turned to see Lariska holding a squirming Vezon by the throat.

"I caught him sneaking down a side tunnel," the Dark Hunter said.

"Let us track down that traitor," snarled Roodaka. "I want his shattered body beneath my heel."

"We're here to do a job," Brutaka replied. "We keep moving. All of us," he added, looking hard at Vezon.

The tunnel proved to be far more than a mere pathway. It opened upon a vast underground cavern spanned by a narrow bridge made of fibrous protodermis.

Down below, the floor was littered with a massive tangle of what looked like dead branches intertwined with each other. Deep channels had been carved into the walls by lava flows over the centuries. Strange flying Rahi hung from the ceiling, their six eyes blinking slowly at the sight of intruders into their realm.

"Remind me not to let Makuta Krika arrange for my next pleasure trip," muttered Spiriah.

"This whole island is volcanic," said Brutaka. "Minor eruptions over the years, but nothing major. Tahu and Kopaka are supposed to have taken care of the problem. Otherwise, we would probably be flash fried by now."

"No Carapar, no Takadox," said Vezon in a sing-song voice. "Who will go next? Spiriah the Sullen? Brutaka the Boorish? Vezon the Vanquisher? Or Lariska..."

The Dark Hunter whipped out a dagger and flung it into the stone right at Vezon's feet. The mad half-Skakdi turned to her, smiling, and said, "Or Lariska, the wise, wonderful, and gloriously homicidal."

Brutaka led the way across the bridge. At the far side, light spilled through a narrow opening.

The symbol of the Brotherhood of Makuta was seared into the stone beside that portal. Someone — maybe Krika, maybe Miserix — had marked their path, so long ago.

"What are we going to do with this legendary Makuta when we find him?" asked Roodaka. "What makes you think he will help the likes of you?"

"Miserix hates the Brotherhood for turning on him," Brutaka replied. "He would ally with three Matoran and an Ussal crab if it would get him revenge on his fellow Makuta."

"And so what will he be for you?" Roodaka pressed. "A general? A hero? A symbol around which to rally resistance to the Brotherhood?"

Brutaka shook his head.

"Nothing quite so grand. He'll be a weapon, like a Rhotuka launcher or a ghost blaster. And we're going to aim him right at the Makuta fortress on Destral."

Roodaka smiled. "And who, might I ask… are 'we'?"

Brutaka smiled back, the grin of a Kavinika about to feast.

"Now, now… what you don't know won't cut you in two and dump you off this bridge."

"I hear something," said Lariska. "Up ahead… it might be a voice… or the rumble of the volcano."

"I hear something too," said Vezon.

"Shut up," replied Roodaka.

"And I see something as well," Vezon continued. "But since you aren't interested…"

"We're not," Roodaka snapped.

"Personally, I always find my comments and observations most interesting," Vezon rambled on. "You haven't truly lived until you have seen the world through the eyes of madness. Why, half the time I don't know if what I see is what's really there, or what I wish was there… or what I pray, I beg, I plead is not."

"Why did we bring him again?" said Spiriah.

"He breaks up the monotony," said Lariska.

"I'd like to break something much more satisfying," hissed Roodaka. "I hear Skakdi make a most appealing sound when you snap them into pieces."

"But, since you seem to have no interest," Vezon continued, utterly disregarding his teammates' comments. "Well, then, I won't tell you that the floor is moving. You can find out on your own."

"The floor is…?" Brutaka repeated.

He looked down. Far below, the tangled growth of dead branches had indeed begun to shift. The reason why rapidly became clear: they weren't branches at all, but the twisted limbs of thousands of crimson insects, now disentangling themselves from each other. Apparently, it was time to wake up and they were ready for their morning meal.

Swifter than anyone could have predicted, they began to swarm up the walls of the canyon on every side. In an instant, they had blocked the openings on both ends of the bridge. The surrounding rock was now gone, buried beneath a skittering sea of red and thousands of unblinking, predatory eyes.

The Makuta concentrated, triggering his power to control Rahi beasts. Nothing happened, other than restless stirring among the insects. After a few moments, Spiriah gave up in frustration.

"They're already under the control of a more powerful will. It must be Miserix."

Brutaka gestured toward the wall of insect life that blocked the way they had come.

"Then I guess you're not leaving." He turned to Lariska. "And we're fighting. You stay back with Vezon. Roodaka, Spiriah and I will lead the way."

"No, no, no," said Vezon, shaking his head. "Too late to apologize. Much, much too late."

Brutaka scanned the cavern with narrowed eyes. The glowing eyes of the insects all around made it feel as if he were trapped in some lunatic starfield. Behind him, he could hear Vezon humming softly to himself, as if out for an afternoon stroll.

"Do we fight our way out of here?" asked Lariska, hand on the hilt of her dagger.

Brutaka's answer was to turn to Spiriah.

"Okay. You control Rahi. Make them clear a path."

"On one condition," said Spiriah. "Once I do, I go free. I turn right around and march out, take the boat – if Takadox hasn't already – and leave. And I never see or hear from any of you, or anyone associated with you, again."

"I wasn't asking you," replied Brutaka. "I was telling you."

"I am a Makuta," said Spiriah. "Disgraced, perhaps; a victim of jealousy and prejudice, most definitely. But I will not be dictated to by some obnoxious, insane…"

Brutaka hit Spiriah a solid blow in the mask, knocking the Makuta over the side of the narrow bridge. Spiriah caught on to the span, just barely, and hung in space.

"I think this is what they call 'in no position to deal,'" said Brutaka. He triggered his mask power, opening a dimensional portal in space just below Spiriah's feet.

"If I move that opening just a little bit further toward you, you'll find yourself in a dimension full of beings made of solid light. Know what they eat there? Shadow. You'll be a food bank for them, Spiriah, but I have to warn you – they're always hungry. And they don't close their mouths when they chew."

Spiriah said nothing. Instead, he reduced his density and floated up and away from Brutaka's portal. Then he drifted back down to the bridge and turned solid once more.

"I'll do it," he said. "Then I leave. I advise you not to try and stop me."

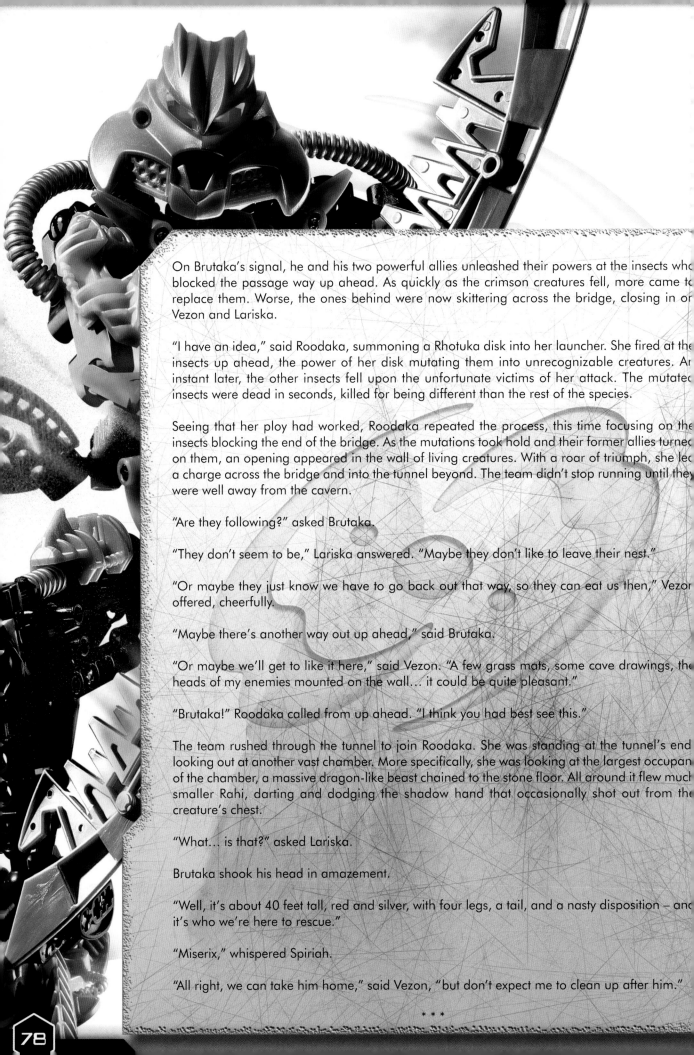

On Brutaka's signal, he and his two powerful allies unleashed their powers at the insects who blocked the passage way up ahead. As quickly as the crimson creatures fell, more came to replace them. Worse, the ones behind were now skittering across the bridge, closing in on Vezon and Lariska.

"I have an idea," said Roodaka, summoning a Rhotuka disk into her launcher. She fired at the insects up ahead, the power of her disk mutating them into unrecognizable creatures. An instant later, the other insects fell upon the unfortunate victims of her attack. The mutated insects were dead in seconds, killed for being different than the rest of the species.

Seeing that her ploy had worked, Roodaka repeated the process, this time focusing on the insects blocking the end of the bridge. As the mutations took hold and their former allies turned on them, an opening appeared in the wall of living creatures. With a roar of triumph, she led a charge across the bridge and into the tunnel beyond. The team didn't stop running until they were well away from the cavern.

"Are they following?" asked Brutaka.

"They don't seem to be," Lariska answered. "Maybe they don't like to leave their nest."

"Or maybe they just know we have to go back out that way, so they can eat us then," Vezon offered, cheerfully.

"Maybe there's another way out up ahead," said Brutaka.

"Or maybe we'll get to like it here," said Vezon. "A few grass mats, some cave drawings, the heads of my enemies mounted on the wall… it could be quite pleasant."

"Brutaka!" Roodaka called from up ahead. "I think you had best see this."

The team rushed through the tunnel to join Roodaka. She was standing at the tunnel's end looking out at another vast chamber. More specifically, she was looking at the largest occupant of the chamber, a massive dragon-like beast chained to the stone floor. All around it flew much smaller Rahi, darting and dodging the shadow hand that occasionally shot out from the creature's chest.

"What… is that?" asked Lariska.

Brutaka shook his head in amazement.

"Well, it's about 40 feet tall, red and silver, with four legs, a tail, and a nasty disposition – and it's who we're here to rescue."

"Miserix," whispered Spiriah.

"All right, we can take him home," said Vezon, "but don't expect me to clean up after him."

* * *

TOA NUVA TAHU

Returning to Karda Nui was particularly difficult for Tahu Nuva. Of all the Toa, only he had clear memories of their last visit here, when he tricked the others into remaining in the Codrex for 100,000 years. It is not something he is proud of, though he knows it had to be done. Had the Toa Nuva been out adventuring during that time, and one of them been killed, they might never have achieved their destiny and awakened Mata Nui.

Tahu led the Toa squad that traveled to the swamps of the core. Their mission was to find the Mask of Life, find the keystones to open the Codrex, and deal with any Makuta they might find. Tahu soon discovered that creative use of his power would be necessary here, such as when he used his flame to explosively ignite swamp gas and stun Makuta Gamprah.

Tahu Nuva wears adaptive armor provided him by Artakha, which is equipped with four powerful jet rockets for speed. He carries an adaptive weapon which has taken the form of a Nynrah ghost blaster, capable of creating any object the user wills out of pure energy. He is also armed with a rotating fire blade. He wears the Kanohi Hau Nuva, the Mask of Shielding.

The Toa Nuva of Fire has since returned to Metru Nui. He is now in overall command of all surviving Toa in the universe.

SWAMP OF SHADOWS

Shortly after arriving in Karda Nui, the Toa Nuva decided to split their forces. Kopaka, Lewa and Pohatu remained to defend the Av-Matoran in the sky villages, while Tahu led Gali and Onua to the swamp below. No one knew what they might find there, as the mist that separated swamp from sky was impossible to see through. Even the Matoran had only gone to the swamp when they had to, and that was when there were no Makuta in the core.

Realizing just how vast the swamp really was, Tahu's team decided to split up. The Toa Nuva of Fire was the first to spot the Codrex, but when he tried to take a closer look, he ran into a force field which knocked him unconscious. Helpless, he lay in the mud as Makuta Krika rose from the swamp to feed on his energy.

Tahu awoke just in time, but he was badly weakened. Krika told him that Makuta hated Toa because Toa were what they could only pretend to be – true heroes who did the right thing for no other reason than it was right. And so they got the honors the Makuta wanted for themselves. Krika told Tahu Nuva he was going to kill him, but before he could act, Tahu shot a bolt of flame into the air – a call for help.

Little did he know that Onua and Gali were both in need of help themselves, as they fought their own battles in the

Mutagenic waters of Karda Nui swamp

TOA NUVA ONUA

Onua has always been considered one [of] the wisest of Toa, and he showed why [in] Karda Nui. From the start, something c[ould] not feel right about this adventure. The T[oa] Nuva were outnumbered and certain[ly] outpowered by the Makuta, yet someho[w] they had avoided destruction. It almost f[elt] as if, despite their ferocious attacks, t[he] Makuta were holding back. Onua cou[ld] not help but wonder why.

Unable to find an answer, he concentrat[ed] on carrying out the mission. Onua's pow[er] over earth saved the Toa more than on[ce] in the swamp, and he was the first [to] discover the function of the Nynrah gho[st] blasters. Makuta Gorast tried repeatedly [to] convince Onua to switch sides, claimin[g] that he would enjoy having a "spirit [as] black as his armor." But Onua refuse[d,] prepared to give up his life to fulfill t[he] team's destiny, if necessary.

Like Tahu, Onua wore adaptive arm[or] equipped with high-tech wings and rockets. He carried a Nynrah ghost blast[er] and a multi-resistant shield. He wore th[e] Kanohi Pakari Nuva, the Mask of Strengt[h.] Onua is currently on Metru Nui, task[ed] with transforming the Archives into [an] impenetrable fortress.

Toa Onua's search for keystones had so far turned up nothing. Stopping to rest for a moment on a spit of mud, he spotted a giant Nui-Kopen wasp coming to attack him. He swatted it into the swamp, then watched as the waters mutated the insect into a monstrous version of itself. Onua realized that something in the water had caused the change – but before he could defend himself, he was attacked from behind by Makuta Bitil. The Makuta used his own ghost blaster to take over all the mechanical parts of Onua's body.

Bitil revealed his mask power to Onua, resulting in a horde of duplicates of Bitil appearing from nowhere. They took Onua to Krika's lair, but Krika was not there. While they were on that island, the effects of the ghost blaster wore off. Onua caused an explosion of mud to engulf the Makuta and flew off. When the original Bitil pursued, Onua used his ghost blaster to create an energy sphere around the Makuta. Trapped, Bitil fell into the swamp.

Onua knew he had to warn the others that the Makuta were in the swamp. But how to find them? That problem was solved when he spotted Tahu's fireball soaring up through the sky. He knew Tahu would never call for help unless it was an emergency.

He flew off to aid the Toa of Fire, but before he could reach him, he spotted another Toa who needed his help...

Past and present Bitils

OA NUVA GALI

ven in the worst of times, Gali Nuva al-
ays tried to be a voice of reason, looking
r peaceful solutions to problems. Some
f that changed in the days before the Toa
ame to Karda Nui. Forced to battle Icarax
r the Staff of Artakha, Gali unleashed a
dal wave that destroyed the realm of
arzahni. She had never caused such
avoc before with her elemental powers,
ut there had been no choice. Like it or
ot, the Toa were at war, and she was
ping to have to fight.

lthough she had known the fight
etween the Toa and the Makuta had to
me someday, it still filled her with dread.
e forces were both so powerful that their
onflict might destroy Karda Nui, even the
ntire universe. Neither side would hold
ack, neither side would surrender, and it
eemed no mercy could be shown. She
ondered if the Toa could even hope to
ick to most important part of their code:
at Toa would never kill their enemies.

ali Nuva wore a suit of adaptive armor
ith two powerful, foot-mounted jets. She
as armed with a Nynrah ghost blaster,
nd wore the Kaukau Nuva, the Mask of
ater Breathing. Although she used her
emental power a great deal in Karda
ui, she had to exercise great control to
ake sure the mutagenic water did not
rike her allies.

e is currently on Metru Nui. At Tahu's
equest, she is engaged in research in the
reat Temple, hoping to learn the secrets
f the Great Beings who created Mata Nui.

ali Nuva was the first Toa to spot one of the keystones, wrapped up in the tendrils of a swamp plant. She was
bout to retrieve it when some sixth sense warned her to turn around. It was just in time, as Makuta Gorast was
ving to attack!

furious battle followed. Gali took a chance, trapping Gorast's head inside a sphere of water. To her surprise,
e succeeded in cutting off the Makuta's air (the effects of the swamp waters had changed Gorast so that she
w needed to breathe). But that was not enough to
op the Makuta. Finally, Gali used her power to
crease the moisture in the ground beneath Gorast's
et. The Makuta made no effort to free herself,
steading sinking beneath the mud. Gali couldn't
elieve anyone would let themselves perish like that.

he next instant, Gorast erupted from the ground
ehind Gali. The Makuta attacked, starting to drain
ali's light from her. Fortunately, Onua flew by at just
at moment. Spotting the trouble, he grabbed Gorast,
ted her high into the air, and smashed her down to
arth. Realizing there was nothing to be gained by the
ght, Onua chose to rescue Gali and fly to where he
ad seen Tahu's fireball.

he only hope the Toa Nuva had now was to stand
gether.

Gorast attacks Gali

MAKUTA POWERS

The Makuta had many powers but in the bodiless energy form can use only psych powers, such as illusion or telepathy. powers are accessible to them only wh their bodies are sheltered in their armour.

Some of these, including shapeshifting, a not available to the Mistika Makuta due their mutation by the swamp water. T complete list of powers includes:

ACCURACY
Can strike the smallest target at a gre distance or in any environment or conditio

ADAPTATION
Instantly adapts to take maximum advanta of any condition or situation.

ANGER
Has the power to turn anyone, even To against one another in anger.

CHAIN LIGHTNING
Controls devastating bolts of chain lightni that leap between multiple targets.

CHAMELEON
Has the ability to become completely invisib in any environment.

CONFUSION
Extended proximity can reduce anyone ever Toa Nuva to mindless babbling.

CYCLONE
Has the power to create and control power cyclones at will.

DARKNESS
Has the power to consume all light (apc from Takanuva's light) in a large area.

DENSITY CONTROL
Complete control over own density, able turn intangible or protosteel hard.

DISINTEGRATION
Has the power to reduce even protodermis dust.

DODGE
Impossible to physically strike, no matter ho swiftly or powerfully.

MAKUTA KRIKA

Makuta Krika was always a reluctant part of Teridax's great plan. When he pondered the future, he saw nothing b destruction. Either the Toa would win and the Brotherhood would be wiped out, or the Makuta would win – but h doubted that would lead to happiness. Deep down, he felt that, somehow, rule by the Brotherhood would lead nothing but fear and death. Still, he didn't believe there was much he could do against the might of Teridax and h loyal followers. So when Teridax ordered him to Karda Nui, he went; when Antroz placed him in command of th Makuta in the swamp, he accepted.

As the mission continued, his doubts grew. He kidnapped Gali and tried to convince her to flee Karda Nui, believir that if the Toa Nuva were to split up, they could not achieve their destiny and wake up Mata Nui. Later, he joined wi Icarax in an attempt to frustrate Teridax's plans by destroying the Codrex and killing the Toa inside.

Krika was trapped in an insectoid form by the power of the swamp waters. He was able to change his density so th he could pass through solid matter, but if he did not absorb energy from other beings or the world around him, h would become permanently ghostly. He carried a Nynrah ghost blaster and wore the Kanohi Crast, the Mask Repulsion. This mask could repel anything Krika chose, even the ground, allowing him to fly.

Upon discovering that an energy storm would consume all of Karda Nui when Mata Nui awakened, Krika tried warn the other Makuta. Gorast refused to believe his story, branded him a traitor to the Brotherhood, ar killed him.

ELASTICITY
can stretch incredible lengths in the blink of
an eye.

ELECTRICITY
powerful electrical field can be controlled to
surround or stun distant objects or creatures.

FEAR
has the power to bring fear to the hearts of
even the Toa Nuva.

FIRE RESISTANCE
strong enough to withstand the heat of Tahu
Nuva's magma swords.

GRAVITY
uses gravity control to crush any object in vi-
sual range.

HEAT VISION
powerful long-range heat vision can ignite
any object within sight.

HUNGER
able to drain the strength of another and
temporarily add it to its own.

ICE RESISTANCE
impervious even to the cold of Kopaka Nuva's
ice blade.

ILLUSION
can create and control multiple realistic illusions.

INSECT CONTROL
powerful enough to control and command an
entire hive of Nui Rama.

INVULNERABILITY
invulnerable to physical harm from most attacks.

LASER VISION
fires powerful eye-beams that can burn
through solid protodermis.

MAGNETISM
possesses magnetic powers strong enough to
tear a slab of protodermis in two.

MIND READING
powerful enough to invade the mind of a
Turaga or Toa Nuva.

MOLECULAR DISRUPTION
has the power to utterly disintegrate any in-
organic object with a touch.

MAKUTA BITIL

Although Bitil had some skill at creating insect Rahi, his true desire was to be a warrior like Icarax or Gorast. Although he was never as good as they, he was aggressive, daring, and ruthless. He followed Teridax because he saw a chance to rule a universe. Yet, despite having every advantage, he was outfought by the Toa Nuva in Karda Nui, who successfully used their wits against his greater power.

Although Bitil was trapped in his insectoid form, he did not suffer as bad a mutation as Krika and Gorast did (seeing what happened to them, he got out of the swamp before it could do too much to him). Heavily armed with blades and spiked armor, he still preferred to rely on his ghost blaster whenever possible. It was far easier to defeat a foe who could not fight back.

Bitil's greatest source of power was his Kanohi Mohtrek, the Mask of Duplication. It allowed Bitil to summon versions of himself from the past to fight alongside him. There were restrictions, however. The past versions could only stay in the present for as long as Bitil could maintain concentration. When they returned to the past, they would remember nothing of the future. And if a past self was killed in the present, Bitil himself would cease to exist.

When the energy storm erupted in Karda Nui, Bitil refused to help Antroz or any of others escaped. He tried and failed to escape the storm, finally being disintegrated by it.

PLANT CONTROL
Has total control over any plants in the area.

PLASMA
Has the power to instantly melt any object in vapour.

POISON
Dangerously toxic even to a Toa Nuva.

POWER SCREAM
Power scream shatters stone and can be hea all across the island.

QUICK HEALING
Quickly heals any physical or elemental blow.

RAHI CONTROL
Has absolute control over every living Rahi in t near area.

SHAPESHIFTING
Has total control over its own shape, although mass cannot change.

SHATTERING
Has the power to create explosions in t immediate area.

SILENCE
Aura of silence is powerful enough to temporar deafen a Toa Nuva.

SLEEP
Has the power to instantly put an entire villag into deep sleep.

SLOWNESS
Able to rob even a Toa Nuva of all speed as lor as it remains nearby.

SONICS
Blasts distant objects with powerful waves sonic force.

STASIS FIELD
Has the power to freeze a creature near-permanent stasis through eye contact.

TELEPORTATION
Has the power to teleport itself through any we or other structure.

VACUUM
Has the power to create gale-force winds instantly reverse their flow.

WEATHER CONTROL
Can manifest powerful, dangerous thunde storms and blizzards at will.

MAKUTA GORAST

Of all the Makuta, Gorast was the most fiercely loyal to Teridax and his plan. To her, nothing was more important tha its success – not her life, not the lives of the other Makuta, not the universe itself. She was truly fearless and nothir could shake her faith in her leader. Any Makuta who dared to betray the glorious cause for which she fought cou expect no mercy. During the final battle, she killed both Krika and Icarax as punishment for their traitorous actions

Gorast had purposely chosen one of the most dangerous and difficult areas to rule, the section of the souther continent that included the fearsome Tren Krom Peninsula. She alone had dared to challenge the acid falls and dor battle with the monstrous creations of Tren Krom himself. Gorast demanded total obedience from those in her domai and there was only one punishment for those who failed to comply: death. As a result, Mutran and Chirox found the could often find volunteers for their experiments from her region, as the inhabitants would do anything to get awa from her. (This stopped when Gorast destroyed Chirox's lab on Destral and threatened to do the same to him.)

Trapped in her insectoid form, Gorast had to drain light from other living things in order to survive. While she cou feed off the light of swamp Rahi, the meals were too small to sustain her for long. That was why she targeted the To either by direct attack or by trying to lure them into her clutches. Gorast had four arms ending in claws and carrie a Nynrah ghost blaster. She wore the Kanohi Felnas, the Mask of Disruption, which could make the powers of othe run wild.

Gorast was killed when the energy storm swept over Karda Nui. Shocked at the turn of events, she made n attempt even to try to escape, simply sat in the mud and waited for the end.

TAKANUVA

Having survived an attack by a shadow leech on Metru Nui, Takanuva found his powers changed. Though he was still the Toa of Light, much of his light had been drained, leaving darkness in its place. As a result, he could now fire light only from his left hand, and shadow from his right. Upon his arrival in the universe core, he grew larger, as his body absorbed the energies of Karda Nui.

Takanuva wore the Kanohi Avohkii, the Mask of Light. He carried a power lance and a Nynrah ghost blaster, both of which he acquired in an alternate dimension before arriving in Karda Nui.

* * *

Dark Mirror

Dispatched by the Order of Mata Nui via the dimensional powers of Brutaka's Kanohi Olmak on a vital mission to Karda Nui, Takanuva finds himself in an alternate universe. Here, Toa Tuyet was able to seize power and turn the Toa into a military force that smashed the Brotherhood of Makuta and the Dark Hunters. But she has become a dictator and her Toa a brutal force who suppress all dissent. Takanuva joins a rebellion against her rule, finally facing the powerful Toa of Water in single combat…

Toa Tuyet stood over the battered, semi-conscious body of Takanuva, Toa of Light. He did not stir. Being blown through half a dozen walls by a focused tidal wave would do that to you. Tuyet smiled.

"Pathetic, truly pathetic. If you are an example of what Toa are like in your universe, it's a wonder you haven't all been hunted to extinction by now."

The ruler of the Toa Empire slipped off her Mask of Intangibility, and replaced it with the Kanohi Olmak, the mask Takanuva had come seeking. This mask alone had the power to open gateways to inter-dimensional space, and it was Takanuva's only hope of escaping this twisted world.

"Your friends outside are dead, or soon will be. I admit I was surprised to find they still had some fight left in them after 3500 years. But they can't be allowed to rob the Matoran of the peace I have brought them."

Takanuva managed to get to his hands and knees, rubble sliding off his back as he did so. He looked at Tuyet with eyes that held equal parts of contempt and pity.

"Peace?" he said in disbelief, "Is that what you call perverting the Toa into secret police, terrorizing the villagers, killing anyone who opposes your rule?"

"I did what had to be done. I made the world right. And who are you to judge me? You are nothing but an alien from some other dimension."

Takanuva hurled a blast of shadow at Tuyet, temporarily cloaking her in darkness. By the time she could see again, he was gone. But his voice came from high above her, saying:

"That's true, my world is messier than yours, more dangerous in some ways. But it is a world that's better, because you're not in it, Tuyet."

The Toa of Water unleashed her power, bringing the ceiling down, but Takanuva was not there. Instead, he sprang from the opening at the far end of the hall, hurling blinding light at Tuyet as he made a grab for her mask. She spun, caught him by the arm and threw him hard to the floor.

"I have hundreds of times your power. You are nothing but a lightstone to be ground to dust beneath my heel."

Takanuva attacked again, hurling bolts of shadow and light. To his amazement, Tuyet parried them with ease. Seeing his surprise, she laughed.

"You know, we had no Toa of Light in this universe. We didn't need one. And in a few moments, we will be back to being without one."

Takanuva charged. The next few seconds were a blaze of battle. Lasers turning water to steam, waves crashing against walls, a race to see what would happen first: Takanuva drowning in the tide, or Tuyet drowning in darkness. When the fight was through, Tuyet stood once more triumphant.

"Enough! I have wasted enough time on you. Your rebellion is finished, and now, so are you."

Tuyet was about to strike when a strange sound penetrated the damaged Coliseum. Takanuva raised his head and glanced at a hole in the wall. He saw hundreds - no, thousands - of Matoran marching toward the building, all of them armed. In the distance he could see airships and sea-going vessels carrying other Matoran, Dark Hunters, Vortixx and others. All of them were descending on the city, their eyes fixed on the Coliseum.

"Still think the rebellion is over?" Takanuva asked, "Or maybe it's just beginning."

"The fools. With my power, I can sweep them all away in a flood like no one has seen before."

Takanuva looked right into Tuyet's eyes.

"Then who would there be left to protect? Who would you have made your perfect universe for?"

Tuyet smiled.

"Very clever, Toa. True, a universe with only drowned Matoran would not be of much use to anyone. But they must be taught respect."

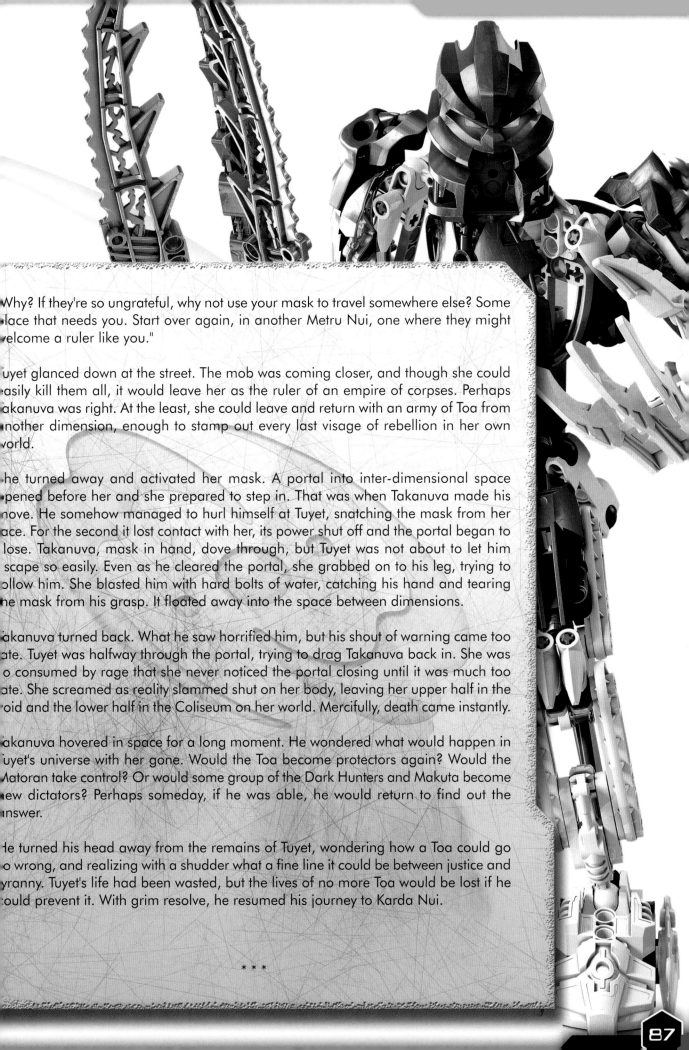

Why? If they're so ungrateful, why not use your mask to travel somewhere else? Some place that needs you. Start over again, in another Metru Nui, one where they might welcome a ruler like you."

Tuyet glanced down at the street. The mob was coming closer, and though she could easily kill them all, it would leave her as the ruler of an empire of corpses. Perhaps Takanuva was right. At the least, she could leave and return with an army of Toa from another dimension, enough to stamp out every last visage of rebellion in her own world.

She turned away and activated her mask. A portal into inter-dimensional space opened before her and she prepared to step in. That was when Takanuva made his move. He somehow managed to hurl himself at Tuyet, snatching the mask from her face. For the second it lost contact with her, its power shut off and the portal began to close. Takanuva, mask in hand, dove through, but Tuyet was not about to let him escape so easily. Even as he cleared the portal, she grabbed on to his leg, trying to follow him. She blasted him with hard bolts of water, catching his hand and tearing the mask from his grasp. It floated away into the space between dimensions.

Takanuva turned back. What he saw horrified him, but his shout of warning came too late. Tuyet was halfway through the portal, trying to drag Takanuva back in. She was so consumed by rage that she never noticed the portal closing until it was much too late. She screamed as reality slammed shut on her body, leaving her upper half in the void and the lower half in the Coliseum on her world. Mercifully, death came instantly.

Takanuva hovered in space for a long moment. He wondered what would happen in Tuyet's universe with her gone. Would the Toa become protectors again? Would the Matoran take control? Or would some group of the Dark Hunters and Makuta become new dictators? Perhaps someday, if he was able, he would return to find out the answer.

He turned his head away from the remains of Tuyet, wondering how a Toa could go so wrong, and realizing with a shudder what a fine line it could be between justice and tyranny. Tuyet's life had been wasted, but the lives of no more Toa would be lost if he could prevent it. With grim resolve, he resumed his journey to Karda Nui.

* * *

THE FINAL BATTLE

After rescuing Tahu from Krika, the three Toa Nuva found themselves in what seemed a losing battle. But hope was rebo[rn] with the arrival of Pohatu, Kopaka, and Lewa. Although the Makuta were united again as well, the Toa were able to dri[ve] them off.

Two new arrivals also added to the Toa's strength, but both brought terrible news. Takanuva arrived in Karda Nui after a lo[ng] journey between dimensions to warn the Toa Nuva of impending doom. When Mata Nui was reawakened, a great energ[y] storm would erupt in Karda Nui, destroying anything that lived. If the Toa Nuva could not find some way to escape, they wou[ld] die there as well. Toa Ignika added to the tension, as it revealed that the Mask of Life was on a countdown to th[e] annihilation of all life in the entire universe.

Using the keystones they had gathered, the Toa Nuva made their way into the Codrex. There they discovered empty sl[ots] where once six Toa canisters had rested. Shocked, they realized that this must have been where they had slept so ma[ny] millennia away, waiting for the call to action.

Curious, Onua studied the strange machinery in the room. Passing his hand in front of a panel, he caused the section of th[e] floor with the canister slots to slowly drop. Down below there was a vast chamber, laid out like the spokes of a wheel. Whe[n] the section of floor settled in the center, huge lightstones rose in a circle from it.

The Toa Nuva flew down to investigate. They discovered three powerful vehicles, long concealed. Built by Artakha when th[e] universe was new, they were the Axalara T9, the Jetrax T6, and the Rockoh T3. Lewa, Pohatu and Kopaka were set to pil[ot] them against the Makuta, but before they could do so, Antroz stole the Jetrax. Lewa and Pohatu pursued him in the Axala[ra] and Rockoh, and a furious aerial battle began.

Kopaka and Onua soon left to join the battle, followed by Takanuva, who was determined to save the Matoran from th[e] coming storm. Tahu was next to go, revealing to Gali before he went his guilt over helping to confine the Toa in the Codre[x] for so much of their lives.

Gali had discovered the process by which Mata Nui could be reawakened, but it was a long one – too long, with the Kano[hi] Ignika soon to eliminate all life. Desperately, she pleaded with Toa Ignika. Only the Mask of Life would have the power [to] bring Mata Nui back to life quickly enough to end the countdown. With the memory of Matoro's sacrifice in its mind, Ignik[a] agreed. It began a descent into the middle of the lightstones.

Outside, the Toa Nuva and Makuta continued their battle. Takanuva had succeeded in curing the shadow Matoran and no[w] directed all of the Av-Matoran to flee Karda Nui and go to Metru Nui, where they would be safe. He was just in time, for th[e] energy storm had begun to gather strength.

The Ignika had begun the process of awakening Mata Nui. Now the Toa Nuva and Takanuva could only hope to escap[e] before it was too late. Climbing aboard the three vehicles, they rocketed across Karda Nui. Looking down, Tahu Nuv[a] realized the storm was going to claim the Makuta – and there was nothing the Toa could do about it, not if they wished [to] live themselves.

"They lit this inferno," said the Toa of Fire. "Let them burn in it."

AXALARA T9

Toa Lewa's craft was the most powerful in the air in Karda Nui, with multi-weapon functions, thick hull armor, and a cockpit designed to directly feed sensor information to the pilot. While not as fast as the Rockoh, it packed a much stronger punch and could take a lot more damage. It was armed with dual blaster cannons, had 24-inch thick protosteel armor, tri-arms equipped with lasers and force field capacitors, and a T9 engine capable of 7 million pounds of thrust.

JETRAX T6

While this powerful cruiser was originally going to be piloted by Kopaka, Makuta Antroz stole it. On its way out of the Codrex, it collided with a huge lightstone and briefly was super-charged with energy, causing its armor to glow yellow. It was equipped with giant jet turbines for greater power, but these could be ejected when additional speed was needed. Armed with three blaster cannons, it gave both the Rockoh and the Axalara a bad time before Kopaka was finally able to recapture it.

ROCKOH T3

Piloted by Toa Pohatu, the Rockoh T3 was designed for both strength and speed. Its combination power dive and ram attack could be devastating, even against multiple enemies. Highly maneuverable, the Rockoh could swerve in and around the huge trees in the swamp – or smash right through them. It featured protosteel armor, retractable wings, a blaster cannon and a T3 engine capable of 2.5 million pounds of thrust.

HOW DOES VICTORY FEEL? WHAT IS ITS SCENT, ITS TASTE? CAN A BEING RELIVE A MOMENT OF TRIUMPH AGAIN AND AGAIN, OR DOES IT BLOW AWAY LIKE ASHES IN THE WIND?

I KNOW THE ANSWERS TO THOSE QUESTIONS. YOU COULD EVEN SAY I KNOW THE ANSWERS TO ALL QUESTIONS NOW – FOR I AM THE ANSWER TO EACH AND EVERY ONE.

THE TOA NUVA AND TAKANUVA ESCAPED KARDA NUI, OF COURSE – I WOULDN'T HAVE HAD IT ANY OTHER WAY. AS FOR THE MAKUTA, THEY WOULD LIVE ONLY LONG ENOUGH TO REALIZE KRIKA HAD BEEN RIGHT. THE TRIUMPH OF THE BROTHERHOOD WOULD BE MY VICTORY, AND I HAD NO INTENTION OF SHARING IT. NO, I SENT ANTROZ AND KRIKA AND THE OTHERS TO KARDA NUI BECAUSE THEY WERE THE MAKUTA MOST LIKELY TO ONE DAY CHALLENGE ME. FAR BETTER TO HAVE THEM OUT OF THE WAY, WITHOUT GETTING MY HANDS DIRTY ELIMINATING THEM MYSELF… AND THE STORM DID THAT QUITE NICELY.

THE HEROIC TOA RETURNED TO METRU NUI, EVEN AS THE GREAT SPIRIT MATA NUI BEGAN TO RISE. OF COURSE, NO ONE BUT I TRULY KNEW WHAT THAT MEANT. I HAD BEEN TO THE PLACES NO ONE ELSE HAD EVER SEEN. I KNEW THE ULTIMATE TRUTH – THAT MATA NUI DID NOT RULE THE UNIVERSE OF THE MATORAN – HE WAS THE UNIVERSE. THE GREAT SPIRIT WAS A VAST BEING OF METAL, A THING OF ARMORED POWER, WITHIN WHOM DWELLED THE TOA, MATORAN, MAKUTA, VORTIXX, SKAKDI, ZYGLAK, AND EVERY OTHER SPECIES. THE LAND MASSES WE DWELLED UPON WERE BUT PARTS OF MATA NUI'S SUBSTANCE, EXISTING TO KEEP HIM FUNCTIONING. WE HAD LOOKED TO THE HEAVENS FOR OUR GREAT SPIRIT, WHEN HE WAS TRULY ALL AROUND US.

NO, FOR THE RESIDENTS OF THE CITY OF LEGENDS, IT WAS ENOUGH THAT HE WAS AWAKE. THEY CELEBRATED. THEY CHEERED. THEY BOWED THEIR HEADS TO GIVE SOLEMN THANKS TO ALL OF THOSE WHO HAD DIED SO THAT THEY COULD SEE THIS DAY… ALL THE WHILE THANKING MATA NUI THAT IT HADN'T BEEN ANY OF THEM CALLED UPON TO DIE. ALL WAS RIGHT IN THEIR PUNY LITTLE WORLD… OR SO IT SEEMED.

The Celebration at the Coliseu

FOUND I COULD NOT WAIT ANY LONGER. I SENT
A CHILL BREEZE THROUGH THEIR ASSEMBLY, AND
MY LAUGHTER WAS IN THE THUNDER OVERHEAD.
REALIZING I STILL LIVED, THE TOA SHOUTED THEIR
DEFIANCE. THE POOR FOOLS STILL DID NOT
UNDERSTAND.

MATA NUI HAD DIED, NOT LONG BEFORE. AS I
EXPECTED, THE TOA MAHRI FOUND SOME WAY TO
RESTORE HIM TO LIFE. I HAD COUNTED ON THAT.
IN THE MICROSECOND BETWEEN WHEN THE BODY
WAS ALIVE ONCE MORE AND MATA NUI'S SPIRIT
RETURNED TO IT, MY OWN SPIRIT ENTERED IT.
ONCE I WAS IN PLACE, MATA NUI'S CONSCIOUSNESS
WAS BARRED FROM RESIDING IN HIS OWN BODY,
FOR THERE CANNOT BE TWO SPIRITS IN ONE
FORM. THE GREAT SPIRIT ROSE, STANDING HIGH
ABOVE THE UNENDING SEA… AND IT WAS I. NO
LONGER DID I NEED TO DREAM OF ONE DAY
RULING A UNIVERSE – I WAS THE UNIVERSE.

WHAT DID I DO NEXT? DID I DESTROY ALL THE
TOA? ENSLAVE THE MATORAN? RAIN FIRE AND ICE
UPON MY ENEMIES? NO. THERE WOULD BE TIME
ENOUGH FOR THAT LATER. I HAD AN INFINITY OF
YEARS WITH WHICH TO TORMENT TAHU, JALLER,
AND ALL THE REST. I WAS THE GROUND THEY
WALKED ON AND THE AIR THEY BREATHED. THEY
COULD NO MORE ESCAPE ME THAN THEY COULD
ESCAPE THE STARLIGHT OR OUTRACE THE WIND.
MY REIGN OF DARKNESS HAD AT LAST BEGUN.

AH, SUCH CHANGES I WOULD BRING. THE RAHKSHI
WOULD BECOME THE ENFORCERS OF MY LAW,
STALKING EVERY SETTLEMENT. VISORAK WOULD
SWEEP ONCE MORE ACROSS THE KNOWN LANDS,
OVERWHELMING ANY RESISTANCE, CRUSHING ANY
HINT OF REBELLION. THE TOA AND THE DARK
HUNTERS WOULD SCATTER BEFORE THE POWER
OF MY SHADOW, REDUCED TO HUDDLING IN
FEARFUL ANTICIPATION OF WHEN I WOULD END
THEIR PITIFUL EXISTENCES.

ONLY TWO THINGS STILL CONCERNED ME. THE
FIRST WAS MATA NUI HIMSELF, WHOSE SPIRIT
MIGHT SOMEHOW FIND A WAY TO… INCONVE-
NIENCE ME. THE SECOND WAS THE MASK OF LIFE
WHICH, IF LEFT ALONE, WOULD SURELY END ALL
LIFE IN MY UNIVERSE.

MY SOLUTION WAS, OF COURSE, BRILLIANT.
I FORCED MATA NUI'S MIND AND SPIRIT INTO THE
MASK, AND THEN EJECTED THE MASK INTO THE
VOID BEYOND THIS UNIVERSE, BEYOND THE
WORLD UPON WHICH I STOOD. I KNOW NOT
WHERE THE MASK WILL LAND, IF IT EVER DOES,
NOR DO I CARE. OF ONE THING, I AM CERTAIN –
I HAVE NOTHING MORE TO FEAR FROM MATA NUI.

BUT THIS UNIVERSE AND ITS PEOPLE HAVE
EVERYTHING TO FEAR FROM ME.

BIONICLE UNIVERSE

N

S

MATA NUI
(ABOVE METRU NUI)

METRU NUI

SEA GATE

KARZAHNI

XIA

STELT

ODINA

NYNRAH

VISORAK

KARDA NUI
(BELOW THE CONTINENT)

DAXIA

ZAKAZ

NORTHERN
CONTINENT

VOYA NUI

TREN KROM RIVER

SOUTHERN CONTINENT

DESTRAL

ARTAKHA

TREN KROM'S
ISLAND

GENERAL INFORMATION

The Matoran universe consists of a series of inter-connected domes of varying sizes. Within those domes are two major continents and many islands, both inhabited and uninhabited, all surrounded by a silver sea of liquid protodermis. Most of the known population lives in the northern section of the universe, with tens of thousands of Matoran on the southern continent alone. Other major races in the universe include the Makuta, the Skakdi, the Vortixx, and the Zyglak. The southern regions of the universe are largely unexplored by the Matoran. It is rumored that there are many strange lands and unknown races living there, but the furthest south anyone has been is the volcanic island of Artidax. What may lie beyond that remains a mystery...

HIDDEN ISLANDS

MATA NUI - situated directly above Metru Nui. A passage to the island opened during the Great Cataclysm. Matoran and Toa lived there until Takanuva defeated Teridax and Takutanuva opened the gate in Mangaia.

KARDA NUI - the "Heart of the Universe" situated directly below the Southern Continent. It is not part of the continent as such - the continent is the roof of Karda Nui's dome.

MAHRI NUI - a part of Voya Nui that broke off during the Great Cataclysm. It sank below Voya Nui in the dark waters of the Pit and was later destroyed when Voya Nui returned to its place on the continent, so it no longer exists.

CONTENTS   PAGE

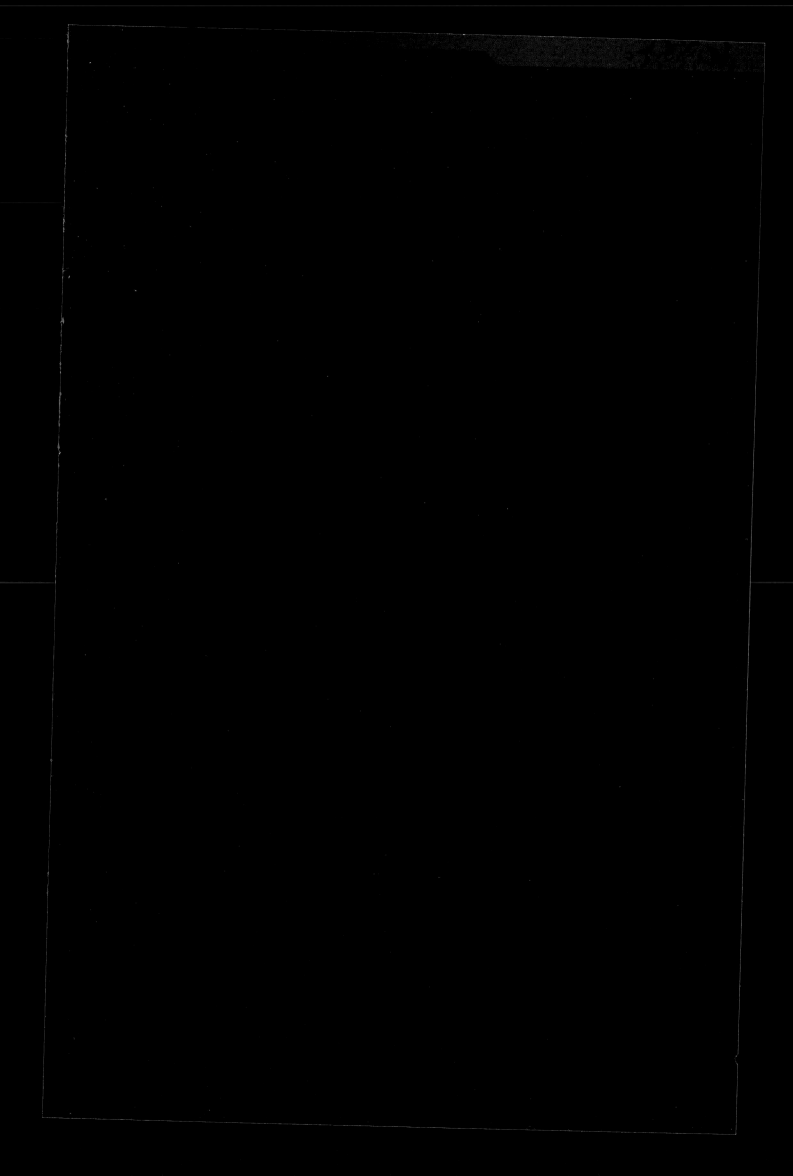

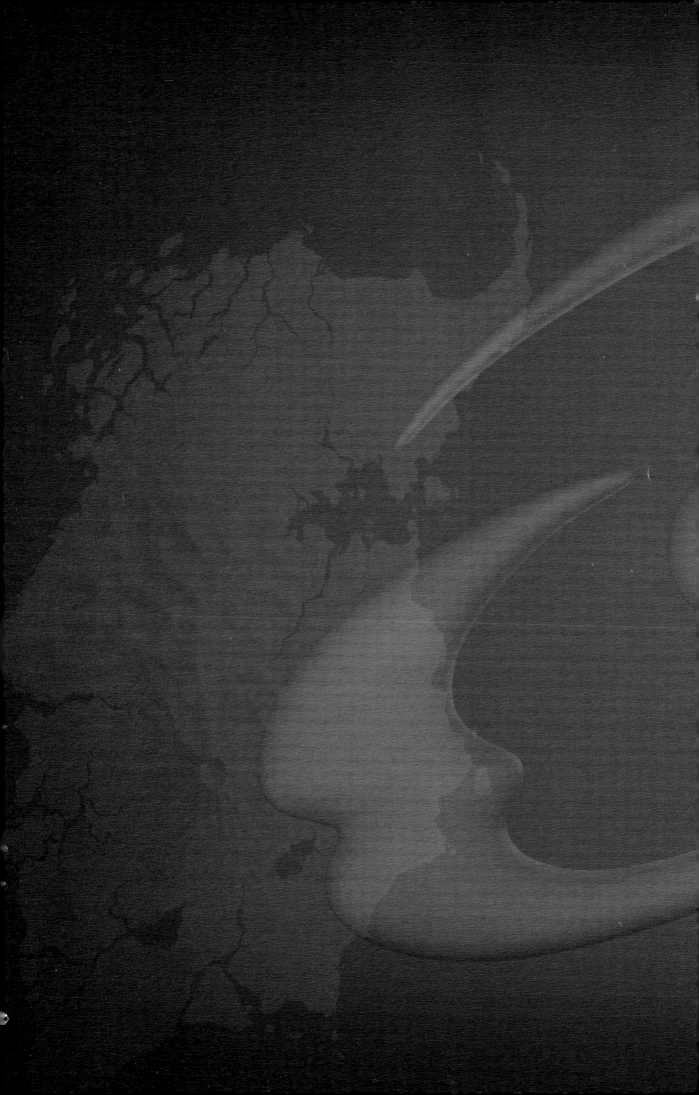